TRAIN

OF *Transformation*

A Novel *by*

David K. Scheiner

PHOENIX, ARIZONA

TRAIN OF TRANSFORMATION

How Forgiveness, Love, Acceptance, Gratitude, and Surrender Will Transform Your Life

A Novel by David K. Scheiner

David K. Scheiner
Phoenix, AZ

Visit our website at www.DavidScheiner.com

Printed in the United States of America

First Edition: December 2021
10 9 8 7 6 5 4 3 2 1

ISBN: 978-1-7323632-0-5

TABLE of CONTENTS

DEDICATION

This book is dedicated to my beautiful
mother Joan, who ignited the spiritual path
deep within me early on and who
left us way too soon.

ACKNOWLEDGMENTS

Most people I have come across want to write a book and I do think they all have a book inside of them just waiting to pour out.

I sat down to write this book as a non-fiction self-help single volume and as you'll see, the universe had other ideas in mind by having a three-novel trilogy pour out from within me in a week and a half.

I had no idea this was about to happen but the Divine Author Within me did. I'd like to first and foremost acknowledge my amazing book coach and friend Tom Bird who provided me with assignments, challenges, and opened me up to learn how to truly write. Our partnership is just getting warmed up.

Next, I want to give wholehearted and sincere thanks to my technical layout, page design, and cover design wizard Marty Marsh. We go way back and have many more projects to tackle together.

I'd like to thank the one and only Bill Worth whose keen eye and attention to copy editing detail proved incredibly valuable.

Writing a personal growth spiritual novel about purpose, possibility, imagination, transformation, and life is an amazing process.

To my family. To my dad, for always being the person I could turn to during those times I needed encouragement and support. To Laura: thank you for the years of support and for always believing in me. To my beautiful girls: Megan, Kira, and Summer. My life became that much richer when you were born. You continue to inspire me and play a big part in my writing. Keep on being the bright lights you are.

To Lucy: If it weren't for you, I'm not quite certain these books would have been born. Thank you for holding the spiritual space open each and every day whereby the words poured through.

To my mom – thank you for lighting the fire and staying connected with me from the other dimension ... this one's for you.

ABOUT
THE AUTHOR

I n the tradition of many a great author, David was meant to write this book, *Train of Transformation.* His journey began in his early youth on Long Island when his mom handed him one impressive spiritual book after another. From Millman, Cohen, Bach, Buscaglia, and Dyer, David read voraciously and had a mystical fire lit within that told him that he too shall make a positive impact and contribution to the world through words he both writes and speaks.

David became a Transformational Life Coach and meditation teacher early on in his youth on Long Island. He then obtained his BA in Sociology from SUNY in upstate New York and his Doctor of Chiropractic degree from Life University.

He has self-published two internationally re-nowned books for the chiropractic profession,

Chiropractic Revealed and *The 8 Laws of Chiropractic Success,* started four holistic health and wellness centers from scratch, and has lectured extensively to the employees of IBM, The Home Depot, Coca Cola, Delta Airlines, and UPS.

He speaks to thousands of university students yearly on campuses worldwide, assisting them in discovering their reason for being in both life and vocation.

When not writing or lecturing, David enjoys spending time hiking, traveling, snowmobiling, walking his dogs, growing inspiring businesses, and relaxing with close family and friends.

Train of Transformation is David's first exciting personal growth novel followed by its two sequels coming soon.

It brings David no greater joy than to have you sit back, relax, and journey along with him and the many wonderful characters and places within these dried, inked pages so you too may recall the reason you came to life.

www.davidscheiner.com

INTRODUCTION

Since as far back as I can recall, the spiritual life was the path that was carved out for me this time around. I don't believe I carved it out. One could say my mom carved it out by handing me personal growth and spiritual books starting at eleven and twelve years old. I devoured those amazing volumes one after the other, put it back in its respective slot on her sacred volume bookshelf, and then she'd pull out another from the shelves under the staircase and hand it over.

"Here, this one would be next. You'll love it!" she'd excitedly exclaim.

Whether it was Millman, Cohen, Bach, Dyer, or Buscaglia, it didn't matter. It was those unique messages within the covers that lit an eternal esoteric flame under me that has sacredly burned since.

My lovely mom didn't carve the spiritual into me. Oh no, she was merely an instrument being used by the innate intelligence of the universe to provide me with arrows, pointers, and signposts to follow. She knew me well, for we were quite similar and would spend hours at a time at the dinner table when all the food and plates were cleared and my sister and father had gone off to do some other activity.

We'd talk about the promise that resided in each human, the potentiality within, to remember who they came here to be for themselves and the rest of the world. We'd talk about someday opening, or at least finding, a school of sorts which would teach people what it means to be human and rediscover their greatness and magnificence from within. She'd bring spiritual weekend retreat workshops to our home on Long Island several times a year where guests would gather and learn from Native American elders and other sacred leaders who'd channel wonderful entities throughout the event. I attended all of them and began to connect even deeper.

I became a Transformational Life Coach and Meditation teacher at a young age because of the exposure to such amazing experiences early on and still perform both to this day in order to guide others deep within themselves and unleash their gifts, abilities, dreams, ideas, and talents to the world. I became quite enamored with the workings of the human mind and psyche and chose to further my education to incorporate the neurological aspects as well. As a Doctor of Chiropractic, I opened several clinics and cared for many thousands of patients over twenty-plus years who've enjoyed the benefits of having their physical and spiritual connectivity's reunited.

Fortunately, my mom held out long enough to see me graduate and soon after, the cancer that had consumed her from all the life stress she held within, had her transition into the formless form she took on before she came here. She continues to communicate with me from the great beyond and our spiritual connection has grown even stronger.

Before she left she said, "Someday you are going to write a book similar to the ones I handed you so many years ago."

I told her, "It's what I've always wanted to do and I thank you for introducing me to such great works of art."

Along with my coaching and meditation teaching, I spend time traveling and lecturing extensively, assisting the young and old in finding their gifts and purpose.

Nothing is more rewarding than seeing the proverbial lightbulb go off when they stand and exclaim, "Ah-hah! I have rediscovered the life I was meant to live!"

It took me four years to find the write space within myself, the write person to guide me, and the write place to sit for a week and a half and have the Divine Author Within me pour out three novels. What I initially thought was going to be a non-fiction self-help book, the universe had other plans by channeling a trilogy of spiritual novels through me.

My friends, those who are seeking and searching on the same spiritual path and plane that I walk upon, and those who are not too far behind, we are not alone. We are kindred spirits and souls, a uniquely mystical and magical collective of ONE riding through space on a transformational train of love and light. "I" wrote this book and it's sequels for you so that you may drop the heavy load from your tight shoulders and remember how to dream once more. Then you'll recall what living is all about.

Easily journey with me aboard a transformational train through a magical tale of Forgiveness, Love, Acceptance, Gratitude, and Surrender, so you too may once again remove the shackles from around your wrists, ankles, and neck, freeing yourself from your self-imposed prison. It is time to recall how you came here to this thing called life to dance in the Now, fully expressed, so you do not go to your graves with your greatness still inside.

May I introduce to you, a story that has been eons in the making, and characters who have been eagerly waiting to meet you. Won't you sit back, relax, and with your internal fireplace aglow, sip your favorite hot beverage while you flip these pages and become transported into a world that you have always wished to visit? It's here, now, calling for you and has been specially created with you in mind.

— *David*

"There's a bigger purpose for us in this mad world. Let's get busy finding what it is!"

CHAPTER ONE

EMPTY FEELING INSIDE

As I sit, this late Friday afternoon, in the tiny 10-by-12 office behind my beautifully painted light blue, chocolate brown, and pine green antique knee-holed Blue Mazarin wooden desk, that familiar pit at the bottom of my stomach began shouting at me.

"There's a bigger purpose for us in this mad world. Let's get busy finding what it is!"

Typically, I'd shrug that voice off and dive deeper into making my outdoor enthusiast customers more inspired, empowered, and motivated to go off into the great outdoors and soak up everything this beautiful world has to offer. I'd recommend adrenaline-rushing trips for them, like trekking on Everest in Nepal, where they'd pass by the magical Gokyo lakes at the foot of the Ngozumpa Glacier or soar over the Tungurahua volcano while paragliding in Ecuador.

I'd book meetings with them months in advance where we'd sit together in this tiny room scouring online over the multitude of excursion opportunities while sipping hot green tea and delighting in a variety of toasted bagel options with their accompanying cream-cheese shmear. We'd sit back, relax, make jokes, and plan their dream trip of a lifetime. Then I'd sell them the necessary equipment for their voyage and they'd email me photos while on their unforgettable journeys.

I was quite happy for the first four or five years clicking the left button on my mouse, scrolling through emailed photos of their dream trips to the rainforest in Borneo, diving with the great whites in Australia, or rushing down the grand white frothy rapids of the Mae Taeng River in Thailand. Then something began to shift in me, a deep knowing that if I continued to live my life through my customers' dreams, that mine will become more deeply embedded in my soul and eventually become lost in there forever.

This shift in me created a feeling of despondency where I lost interest and became complacent. I stopped sitting with my customers in my office, hired Audrey as a store manager, and trained her to have those planning sessions with them. She became a natural and they loved her. They asked about me for a while, and eventually stopped. The store hasn't skipped a business beat but the outdoor enthusiast beat inside me slowed and eventually came to a halt.

I now sit for eight-to-ten hours each day behind this desk watching as the multiple and varied stacks of bills, invoices, and flyers continue to fill up every square inch of this tiny room. I do take several breaks a day and step outside the office door into the large supply storage room where I keep the excess apparel, footwear, bicycles, ropes, and fitness gear.

Today was no exception. I got up from behind the desk and piles of paper, walked carefully through the maze of manila envelopes and beige file folders built up on the floor, and drifted out onto the cement floor of the storage room. I grabbed my lavender foam yoga mat off the metal storage shelf just outside and to the left of my office door and unrolled it.

I stood lightly on the purple foam and went deeply into a tree pose and then warrior. These were gradually followed by mountain, down dog, warrior II, and bridge. The beads of sweat built up as did the invigoration and momentum. After 30 minutes of this ancient practice, I laid on my back with arms and legs spread slightly in Savasana pose.

I continued my deep breathing, the sweat intensified, and I sank into the relaxing yoga nidra meditation. In my rooted state, I visualized and sensed the store, the customers, my office, and my life in totality. A realization and knowing that a shift was about to occur in my life, traveled up through the floor, into the bottom of my feet, and coursed over my entire nervous system.

I felt a new excitement I had not known for some time. My mind brought me to the multiple personal-growth seminars I had attended over the past 12-months. These seminars and workshops brought me a sense of creativity and varied opportunities to create a future life of my own design.

This recollection jolted me into remembering the seminar I had coming up this evening, which continued throughout the weekend. The two-hour introductory session at the renowned Javits Center in Manhattan began at 6:30 p.m., and if I was going to make it on time, I'd have to get up now, shower in my personal bathroom next to my office, and arrive at the train station to catch the 5:15 p.m. express into Grand Central Station.

I opened my eyes from the deep meditative state, looked around the storage room, and took a visual sensory impression of my surroundings. This practice kept me grounded firmly in the grasp of the present moment. I observed mountain bikes on high-shelf racks, various colored kayaks, roller blades, paddle boards, hiking equipment, clothing, and men's and women's footwear.

The storage room also had a uniquely distinct odor, which reminded me of when I'd walk in and out of the warehouses of the Garment District in Manhattan. It was a smell I greatly enjoyed and in this moment added additional excitement to get into the city that never sleeps.

I rolled up the lavender yoga mat, tucked it neatly onto the silver metal shelving next to my office door, and went back through the paper maze office to buzz Audrey up front.

Sitting with my knees in the hole of the Blue Mazarin desk, I pressed the intercom button on the phone and said to Audrey, "Hey A, I almost forgot about the intro-evening session of the personal-growth workshop in the city tonight. I'm going to grab a shower back here and ride my Cannondale CX-3 to the train station. So no need to be concerned when you see my car out back after you close the shop."

"Okay, sounds great, David. I have everything covered. Enjoy the seminar and I'll look forward to hearing all about it tomorrow."

I kept a change of clothing in my personal bathroom in case something came up and I had to leave from the store. I showered quickly, threw on my 20-year-old tough resilient Levi button-fly faded blue jeans, solid black V-neck T-shirt, Adidas Terrex blue hiking shoes, and grabbed my bike off the storage room floor.

I slipped my backpack over my shoulders, exited my store through the solid heavy grey metal door, and pressed on the two lightweight aluminum magnesium alloy black pedals. I felt the efficient transfer of power from my legs to the bicycle wheels while quickly making my way through the damp neighborhood streets. I deeply inhaled the pleasant aromatic earthy scent generated by the recent rainfall, prompting my quads to pump harder.

That aroma, combined with the airborne mix of

green leaf volatiles from the freshly cut neighborhood lawns, made for an extremely pleasant and invigorating fall late-afternoon ride to the town train station. I approached the street corner at Maple and Elm and let go of the brakes slowly through the turn to maintain proper traction and control the bike on these wet grounds.

I caught a quick glimpse of Joe, the owner of the best pizza joint in town, up ahead sweeping the sidewalk in front of his shop. I heard the sweet sounds of his perfectly harmonized whistling to Frank Sinatra's hit *New York, New York* blaring from inside his restaurant. I turned my face to the right as I passed by and called out, "Hey, Joe, smells great as always!"

"Hey, kid, stop by for a slice on your way back, capisce?"

I locked my bike to the newly installed green bikeep bike dock, which allowed me peace of mind when leaving my bike out in the open at the station.

The loud calls of "All Aboard," came from the tracks above me. I briskly slid my yellow and blue Metro card through the turnstile slot, ran up the dirty wrought-iron flight of steps, and onto the concrete train platform.

With the shiny double metal train doors coming to a slow close, I ran at them, turned my body sideways, and squeezed right through. The doors closed onto my backpack, then opened slightly, allowing me to yank the pack through.

CHAPTER TWO

THE CITY THAT SOMETIMES SLEEPS

The train immediately began to roll forward across the steel beam tracks and I grabbed hold of a rigidly-mounted silver handle above me to keep from falling onto the floor. I slowly glanced my eyes across the car to target my seat and noticed there was an empty row straight ahead on the right side. I walked across the inside of the moving car toward my row, as the soles of my hiking shoes suctioned across the humid and sticky metal floor.

I sat on the forward-facing hard plastic beige seat, propped my backpack up on the one next to me, and inhaled through my nose deeply into my abdomen. Looking out the blurry window to my right, I saw the New York City skyline appearing to smile, knowing I was coming to pay her a visit.

What a long day, I thought as I started thinking

about my life purpose and what the reason is for my being here. I again thought about my store, my seven hard-working years where I was completely committed and obsessed to its success. I felt a sense of accomplishment while the familiar pit-in-the-stomach sensation lurked in the background.

No use in focusing on the past, I thought to myself. It was time to reinvent my life and live it with all-out purpose and passion.

I relaxed into the plastic beige frame beneath my body and with heavy eyelids, I felt myself doze off. For a few minutes, while I was transitioning between wakefulness and sleep, I sensed deep within my soul that there was still much more for me to accomplish and bring to the world this lifetime.

The next thing I knew, the air compression underneath produced a loud hostile train-track screeching. Then a large hand palmed my left shoulder and began shaking me out of my dense stupor.

"Wake up son, we're at Grand Central. I need you off the train, I have a tight schedule to keep." I opened my eyes and felt dazed. Hovering over me was a tall train attendant dressed in a navy-blue three-piece suit. The coat, vest, and trousers were ironed to perfection and his black front-brimmed cap fit snugly on his head. His fair skin was freckled, slightly blushed, and his upper lip was entirely covered by his ginger handlebar moustache. I looked to the left and right of him and noticed the car had completely emptied out. "You were zonked out the entire trip into the City, young man. I waited as long as I could. Time to get a move on."

"I'm on my way, pal. Thanks for the extra few minutes of shut-eye." He took the brim of his black cap between his right thumb and index finger and tipped it down in approval.

The nap was just what I needed. I felt refreshed, enlivened and ready to soak in two-hours of positivity, purpose-finding, and possibility. I grabbed my backpack, exited the already opened steel double doors, and walked briskly through the underground catacomb passageways of Grand Central Station.

The white ceramic rectangular subway tiles enveloped me and straight ahead, embedded in the center of the large tiled white wall, was large black lettering that read, " ◀ EXIT LEFT."

I hooked to the left at the broad white tiled wall,

followed the long concrete hallway straight up a small incline, and walked out through the propped open glass and metal doors into the breathtakingly cool and crisp fall day in New York City.

The smell of dry leaves and a slight firewood odor drifted into my nostrils, followed by the incredible aroma of hot pretzels cooking over fire briquettes in a shiny metal shopping cart. Saliva pooled up at the inside corners of my mouth. Alas! It was my turn to order.

"I'll take one with mustard, please."

"You want packets or want me to lather on a thick layer of Gulden's?"

"Lather away, my friend. I'm a long-time mustard lover."

"Here ya go. That'll be four dollars and twenty-five cents."

I handed him a five-dollar bill and told him to keep the change. I grabbed a couple of white paper napkins out of the black and silver holder and wrapped my lips across the middle of the baked dough, sinking my teeth deep into the spicy brown deli mustard.

The combination of perfectly baked crispy hot dough, salt, mustard, and crunch propelled me right into that New York state of mind I was longing for. I pressed on in the direction of Central Park and noticed that the people and streets of the city seemed somehow "off." A variety of weeds were growing out of the cracks in the busy streets and the windows of the tall buildings were covered in fine layers of dirt, dust, and mud splotches.

Everyone was walking with their heads down, even those people who were not staring at their not-so-smartphones. Their strides appeared to take on a robotic and machine-like quality. Even with their eyes open, it was as if they were sleep-walking. I walked up to one of them and they did not even stop or notice me. I said, "Yo, do you not even see me over here?"

I brushed off the silence, continued toward Central Park, and enjoyed the next bite of my amazing salted delicacy. This was an appetizer for me at best. My favorite diner was next door to the Javits Center and this is where my internal GPS was guiding me tonight for the pre-event food festivities. My mouth began to water once more as I started to think about their vegan jambalaya that would be in my stomach within a matter of minutes. First, I'd have to get through Central Park.

My two favorite New York City parks are Central Park and Washington Square Park. For me, Washington Square has the best people-watching and Central has more things to do, by far. I'd spend hours at a time there roller blading, watching chess matches, and breathing in the wonderful air on a cool fall late afternoon. There were even picnics on plaid red, black, and white blankets on several occasions with various dinner dates.

I took the final bite of my pretzel, threw the white paper I held it in into the dark green rubber receptacle, and entered the park. I noticed taller and unkempt grass, weeds sprawling in every direction, and huge cracks along the walk paths. Hordes of pigeons surrounded each passerby, and their collective smell was suffocating. The scene was something out of a Twilight Zone episode and I felt like the main character.

A large concrete footbridge was up ahead and several homeless individuals were blocking anyone from passing underneath. I heard them saying, "It'll cost you if you're gonna get by here," and "This is our territory, there's a fee to enter our home." They, like the pigeons, had a horrible odor and perhaps it wasn't such a bad idea to go around them. I simply couldn't, though, because I'd miss my amazingly delicious jambalaya and arrive late to the seminar.

I mustered up some courage, came upon the group and asked, "How much to get by?" "It'll cost ya a hundred dollars," said the person who appeared to represent the entire lot. "How about fifty?" I asked.

"Done," said the leader.

Remember, I'm thinking Twilight Zone and this was playing out exactly that way. After I handed over the cash, everything turned to black and white. It made me feel uneasy and beads of sweat began to collect in the small of my back while others trickled down the sides of my forehead onto my face. I looked around me in a fresh panic and all the other people who were not with the homeless were suddenly dressed in 1950's clothing.

I excused myself from the pack of homeless, and walked under the high-arching bridge. The panic and anxiety left as I glanced at the fancy curved stone architectural walls surrounding me. I was amazed they were graffiti-free and with each stride forward I marveled at the beautiful architectural symbols and mythological characters. Gargoyles and dragons popped out from the stone every few feet where the roof and curved walls met.

It looked and felt as though I was walking through a Norman-esque medieval tunnel, represented by all of the semi-circular arches. When I arrived at the other end and emerged out of the tunnel, the sunlight hit my face and the energy of its rays warmed through me. I became excited when I saw my exit from the park far off to my right but the immediate problem I faced was getting to it. My strides had become super heavy and each one gave me the feeling that I was walking through thick deep mud. I wondered, "Were they working on the bridge above and spilled some wet cement below?"

I saw my feet in front of me but walking became virtually impossible as the feeling of sinking into cement intensified. I reached down and grabbed my right foot with my right hand. It felt normal but for some reason I couldn't get two steps ahead without using all of my strength. I took my hydroflask out of my backpack and poured some water onto my head to cool off and wake me out of this weird state. It felt amazing but my steps stayed the same.

My breathing became short and labored. Panic started to set in, so I closed my eyes where I stood and practiced deep breathing that I had learned at another recent personal-growth seminar. After a few moments a renewed sense of calm came over me so I opened my eyes and set my sights on the exit to my right. I had to get out of this park now and into the diner. Just standing here and thinking about it, I could literally taste the amazing vegan jambalaya.

Okay, now we're getting somewhere, or so I thought. My mind tricked me into feeling I was moving toward the exit when my body wasn't moving at all. I lifted my right thigh with both hands and placed that leg ahead. I then did the same with my left leg. "C'mon legs," I yelled and when I picked my right leg up once more and placed it ahead of the left leg, I was sucked halfway through a portal into another dimension.

CHAPTER THREE

THERE'S A BRIGHT GOLDEN HAZE

I felt and saw the right half of my body in a beautifully colored open meadow and when I looked back to my left, the other half of me was still black and white in Central Park. It was at this in-between point that I experienced myself as an observer of the two halves of myself. As this silent watcher, I had to decide: was I going to force myself back into the Twilight Zone experience of Central Park or propel forward and enter fully through the portal into the unknown? I made the choice to push completely through the portal when I remembered these words from my last seminar, "You have to be okay not knowing."

The tall beige grass was luscious and the smells of poppies, bee balm, and purple coneflower filled the vast meadow. Loud cricket and grasshopper chirps echoed throughout the valley and when I tested my stride, much to my delight I was able to walk normally again. Green dragonflies surrounded me, made faint clucking sounds, and beckoned me to follow them. *I'm good, I got this,* I thought to myself and followed my winged friends forward toward a wide dirt path up ahead.

We arrived at the trail, which was made of fine white sand and beige pebbles. I reached down, picked some up, and slowly let it filter between my fingers. It reminded me of the neighborhood playground sandbox I'd spend hours at a time in as a small boy.

The path felt cushiony under my feet and I noticed an extra bounce in my step. I looked all around and saw the dragonflies, beautiful trees swaying in the distance, varied multi-colored butterflies, and more gorgeous wildflowers. I heard the delicate sounds of rushing river water and waterfalls in the distance and I hoped we were walking in their direction. I took several calming deep breaths and at the same time took a complete visual impression of all natural sights, sounds, and smells around me.

I felt serene, calm, and continued following the dragonflies along the path toward a small clearing up ahead.

The fine sand and small pebbled path became a stone paver trail. My new dragonfly friends bid me farewell and I mimicked their clucking sounds to say goodbye. I walked by myself up a short incline, veered to the left off the stone pavers, and onto a large bed of lusciously thick manicured green grass. It must have just been cut, as the aroma reminded me of a hot August summer day. I looked around for a clear pitcher of ice cold lemonade and an empty cup but there would be no such luck.

A large population of green grasshoppers greeted me at my feet; replacing the dragonflies, they escorted me to beautiful flower beds that rested peacefully to the left of a small stone home. I observed multiple hummingbirds flutter their tiny wings in figure 8 patterns and in that moment time slowed and almost came to a complete stop. It was still moving enough to have me watch as this one particularly beautiful blue, green, and yellow hummingbird drew nectar out of a trumpet creeper. I observed as its long tongue retracted from the flower, coiled up inside the birds' head, and around its skull and eyes. This natural display of Universal Intelligence left me in awe.

The hummingbirds were joined by a kaleidoscope of butterflies who were also flapping their wings and sipping from a variety of colored flowers, using their thin tongues. One in particular caught my attention, flying quite close to my face, and then returning to the others. The six-foot high stone wall behind the flowers, hummingbirds, and butterflies created the perfect backdrop to watch this nature documentary film up close. The wall extended from the front to the back of the property and created a fine natural feel to the estate.

I pivoted on the lawn to the right and observed five tree-like stone stumps. They created a half moon configuration and stuck out at perfect seat height for the average adult. I sat upon the one at the far left and glanced at a small fire-pit just in front of the seats. Multiple pieces of burnt wood, which still gave off a fine hint of smoky fragrance, lay haphazardly atop burnt ash. I looked to my left at the other stumps and sensed the presence of four other entities.

I rose and climbed four stone steps to the richly deep-stained wood front door of the stone home, grabbed the thick rusty knocker, and clanged it forcefully several times. The sound was so loud, it scared the hummingbirds off into the tall eucalyptus trees behind the stone wall. I waited a minute to see if anyone would answer; no one did. The hummingbirds returned, not to the flowers for more nectar, but to where I stood, summoning me to follow them around to the right of the home into the back.

I was happy to follow along with such beautiful new friends. On our leisurely walk to the back yard, one purple, pink, and green tiny bird hovered right in front of my right ear and softly whispered, "Stay the course." I looked at my fine feathered friend and nodded my head in approval.

The back yard was a massive expanse made up of the same finely-cut thick grass. It smelled just as incredible back here as up front, and again I looked around but as luck would have it, there was no pitcher of ice-cold lemonade. Still, my mouth watered at the mere thought of taking in a glass.

On the back facing of the small stone home, there were thick, deeply wood-stained beams lining where the stone walls met the roof tiles. Underneath the beams, on the left side of the back door, were three windows, each divided evenly into four panels of glass. I walked up to them, looked through the kitchen and to the front of the home. I still could see no human signs of life.

I backed away from the home and found the stone paver path once again. This time, I followed it deeper into the back of the property and noticed an old red, rusted swing-set resting upside down and leaning against the six-foot stone wall where it ended and the massive forest began.

CHAPTER FOUR

THE FOREST

At the entrance to the woodland, the stone paver path stopped and another hummingbird whooshed past me, then darted back quickly. It hovered right in front of my face, creating a soft gentle breeze on my skin. "Press on," said the tiny bird, and I followed it between trees so high I could not see their tops.

It had been many years since I was in the presence of the natural giant Hyperion tree. I stopped roughly twenty feet into the wooded area just to look up and marvel at the beauties surrounding me. I walked up to one of the giants, closed my eyes, and pressed my palms onto its rough bark. This particular one exuded a mild-spice aroma with an earthy hint through its cracked "skin." I felt an immense energy coming through the tree and into the depths of my being.

I spoke to it telepathically and thanked it for its

mere presence and aliveness. I sensed a reply of "Namasté," released my palms, opened my eyes and fixed them on the magnificent deep blue sky above. This particular sky was the perfect backdrop for the wooden skyscrapers and flocks of hummingbirds. As I observed the magical and mystical dance between trees, birds, and blue sky, I was unaware of the gaping hole in the forest floor below. My right foot almost stepped into it and twisted minimally inward, which had me place extra pressure on my left foot and propel myself a few steps ahead to avoid disaster.

That was a really close call. I "walked off" the slight discomfort and while my attention was on the level of pain I was experiencing, I failed to notice that I was now completely engulfed by row after row of Hyperion. I turned in slow circles trying to get my bearings and simply couldn't figure out which direction I came from to get to where I now stood. A wave of panic came from the bottom of my feet, through my entire body, all the way to the top of my head.

I likened my situation to the feeling I might get when driving in light snow flurries and without warning, it would immediately turn into a white-out blizzard. I was completely lost, stumped, and the panic intensified.

I recalled the words from a spiritual book I read recently that said, "If you no longer have control over your situation, drop all resistance to it, and accept your present moment as it is."

I felt grateful those words sprang into my head and the feeling of panic somewhat subsided. I then received an intuitive message from the forest to spin in place once again but this time I was to close my eyes. I removed my backpack, placed it on the dirt beside me, raised my arms high into the air, and began to whirl like a dervish. I started to feel grounded and at one with the forest.

With my closed eyes, I picked up the pace and sensed three hummingbirds descend from high above to join me within this circular frenzy. I heard and felt their flight pattern circling counterclockwise three inches directly above me. If you were high-up in the trees looking down, you'd think I was wearing a crown on top of my spinning head.

I continued the whirl and deepened my breathing. The hummingbirds flew faster and a message from the forest entered me; "Worry takes us out of the now. When you surrender to the 'is-ness' of the moment, you begin to remember and experience the stillness within you. Make 'not-knowing' your new friend."

I absorbed the message and felt the ground shake beneath me. The energy of the massive trees made their way deep inside my soul, filling me with grace. I could no longer tell where the forest began or where I ended. All hesitation and resistance to where I found myself ceased and my spinning became one with the rhythm of the moving world around me.

I opened my eyes, gradually stopped rotating, and picked up my backpack. I was now being spoken through by the tall Hyperions, who led me deeper into their angled rows, off to the right. A small clearing appeared and it prompted me to take multiple natural deep breaths. Magically, each inhalation drew the trees toward me and each exhalation blew them away. Being connected with nature at this depth brought a new-found sense of excitement and conscious awareness.

CHAPTER FIVE

THE SACRED ELDER

At this open space before me I was welcomed by a lake which was home to multiple species of fish and turtle. Largemouth Bass, Yellow Perch and Rainbow Trout leaped out of the water and made large splashes, while Red-Eared Sliders basked in the sun's warming rays upon small rocks at the water's edge. Ten feet back from where the water began, large flat stones big enough to lie down on, lined the entire circumference of the lake. I thought about taking a nice peaceful nap but instead I chose my stone, hopped up, and sat down Indian style to enter into stillness with the forest.

I took several deep breaths, brought my head back, and observed a large flock of colorful wild birds flying and singing their beautiful tunes above. They glided and crisscrossed across the lake and settled on high branches in the tree tops opposite from one another.

The same breed of tree surrounded the entire lake and at the back of each large flat stone, a tree was connected. In my seated lotus posture, I leaned back up against the tree, felt its energy connect with mine and my eyelids gradually closed.

The stone beneath gave me a sense of strong support and I felt very grounded. My deep breathing connected me directly with the present moment and I went into an inner body visualization. The tree communicated through the stone I was sitting upon and the message, "When your thoughts take you away, simply bring your attention back to your breathing," came through me. I emptied my mind of all thoughts and was able to connect my breathing pattern with that of the trees. Everything inside and around me slowed its motion, which propelled me even deeper into stillness.

The question, "How do you know you have hands?" came up from the stone's core and through me. I brought my awareness to my hands and sensed them. Then came the question, "How do you know you have eyes?" and I brought my awareness to my eyes and sensed them, too. The questioning sparked me to go deeper into my body and take a wonderful journey within. I connected with and visualized the flow of my blood, the pumping of my heart, and the firing of electrical impulses from my brain down the spinal cord.

I continued on this magical inner-body excursion and connected with the marrow within my bones. I went even deeper, brought my awareness to individual cells, which made my body tingle and come to life more than I've experienced before. The flutter of wings tickled my right ear, breaking my inner-body concentration. I immediately brought my attention back to my breathing and sat still in the enjoyment of how magnificent I felt.

I heard the sound of footsteps flattening and crunching the dry leaves on the ground between the lake and the stone I was sitting upon. My breathing deepened and I saw myself at home as a small child, picking up dry colorful leaves from the ground and with both hands tossing them high into the air above me. I loved the musky sweet smell of the leaves so much that I could literally taste it. The footsteps got closer and instead of opening my eyes to see what was coming toward me I remained still and confident, not knowing.

This time it was not the tree or hummingbird wings providing the message. This was a human voice standing right by the stone where I was meditating: "That's very good. Keep breathing deeper with your eyes remaining closed. Stop trying to make sense of what is happening with you and the world around you. Just allow things to simply be and continue the practice of non-resistance."

I was very curious who this was standing by me and was about to open my eyes when she said, "Keep the eyes closed for now and deepen your breath. In through the nose and out through your mouth. This time make sure that when you inhale through the nose, hold the air in your abdomen for three seconds and then release."

I had to intentionally keep my eyelids pressed tightly together to keep from opening my eyes. I wanted to see who this was so badly and lucky for me her voice started again which temporarily ended my need to see her.

"Stop thinking about me, what I look like, and who I am. Curiosity attempts to get the best of you and everyone else. Simply keep focusing on your breathing. No-thought and no-doing. Only stillness, silence, and being. I am going to join you now on this stone and you will continue this ancient breathing exercise with your eyes closed."

I felt a gentle and purposeful finger-tip contact at the space between my eyes. There were no words spoken; none were needed. She was communicating to me through her fingertip, which had me go back within my body and journey to my heart. I saw my heartbeat slow down and the beautiful rich-red crimson blood pumping easily through its four chambers. I brought my attention over to my lungs and saw the air I was taking in fill them like two balloons.

A wave of gratitude came over me for the miracle I was looking at within my own body and tears began to softly cascade down my face. Her fingertip disconnected from my forehead and she said, "You created that. The problem is that people forget about the phenomenon occurring within their own body. This failure to re-member is initiated when thoughts take over one's life. Along with the workings of the inner body going on auto-pilot, so does the person's entire existence."

The stone began to softly vibrate under us and she asked, "What do you see."

"What do I see? My eyes are closed so I don't ..."

She cut me off and exclaimed, "You do not see with your eyes for they deceive you, the same way you do not hear with your ears. True hearing happens by other means and only when one is engaged in listening. You see with your vision within. Now tell me, what do you see?"

"I see my heart pumping. I see my bones and the marrow within them. I see my lungs filling with air on my inhalation."

"Now, how does visualizing the inner workings of your body make you feel?"

She put extra emphasis on the word *feel* and I told her, "I do not recall having felt this way before. I am feeling a deep and sincere appreciation for my life. A genuine feeling of gratitude and love."

"That is a very good start. Hold those feelings for a bit longer and tell me, where were you coming from when you stumbled upon my stone home earlier?"

What happened next amazed me. I visualized my subconscious mind get triggered by her question, and a pulley system initiated, bringing a pre-programmed automatic response up from the depths of my subconscious. I did not reply and bring that response out of my mouth. Rather, I sat in silence and noticed how the triggering made me feel.

"Now you see how quickly, when one is asked a

question or confronted, automatic and already always listening thoughts distract you. You may also notice a defensive posturing arise, which is the Ego revealing itself."

She was right. It was happening right before my closed eyes. At one moment, I was peacefully visualizing and engaged with the inner workings of my body, and after her question, I was totally distracted. I felt this internal duality dance she was referring to and it brought the image of a machine-like person into my mind. Much like the people walking through the city streets of New York earlier today.

"Enough," said a voice inside my head. I began to open my eyes and she yelled, "Not yet! Keep your eyes closed and continue your deep breathing. I am going to rub some peppermint essential oil between your eyes and when I tell you to, you may open them."

I felt the finger administering and massaging the oil in. It smelled and felt incredible. The added plus was the removal of slight tension in my head. I wasn't certain if I would be able to open my eyes when she gave me the okay because of how wonderful the forehead massage was.

"What you are thinking regarding massage is not

what I am doing. Let your thought go and stop trying to make sense of any of this. Simply inhale the invigorating aroma of peppermint and now you may slowly open your eyes."

My eyelids opened and as I observed her finger rubbing peppermint oil between my eyes, I was at a loss for words for what sat directly in front of me. She was absolutely the most beautiful person, inside and out, that I had ever laid eyes upon. Her long white shiny hair was in a thick braid that draped down her backside to the waist. She had dark, rich, deep-brown eyes and extremely high cheekbones. Her beauty made me feel awestruck and quite stunned, as if I were in the presence of ancient Roman royalty.

I could tell she knew what I was thinking when she said, "Think nothing of it. What matters is what is on the inside and if you are going to accomplish what you've set out to do here, time and focus is what is of the essence."

I could not say a word because I was listening to her from a deep place within me where my true essence resided. We held sustained eye contact and were staring into one another's eyes like two lovers standing at the altar.

"What is it?" she asked.

"Well, it's just that ..." she cut me off again.

"We have no time for small talk. What there is time for is the work ahead of us. For you, there's a lot of healing and self-discovery to do."

She brought forward a brown leather pouch, untied its thin strings, and poured some ash onto the stone between us. Pointing to the tree behind me, she said, "This sacred ash is from one of these tall Hyperion's that falls approximately every 250 years, incinerating instantaneously when it hits the ground."

She rubbed a tiny amount onto my third-eye chakra and continued, "When it cools, this ash is collected by a few of us that use it for ancient and sacred purposes. Mixing it with the peppermint oil already between your eyes, you will have a renewed and enhanced vision for challenging times."

I became caught up in thought and immediately wondered what challenging times she meant.

"Focus!" she exclaimed.

I took a long deep breath in and blew it out while she removed another item from the pouch.

"Take this crystal and hold it in your right hand.

Keep your palm open and allow it to naturally rest there. It will do what only it knows to do."

I did exactly as she instructed with the small lavender stone and observed as she gently blew three soft breaths onto my outstretched palm. The crystal began illuminating a soft purplish hue and one after the other, purple butterflies emanated from the palm of my hand and rose up high to join the hummingbirds at the treetops.

My face must have taken on a look of wonder and amazement because she asked, "What is it? Have you not ever heard of, seen, felt, touched, or smelled sacred ancient mysticism in your life?"

This question pierced me like an arrow shot straight through my soul. I thought about my life and wondered if I in fact had been living up to this point or merely surviving. I then thought about my store and the endless days, hours, weeks, and years I've spent in my sardine can ten-by-twelve office. A nauseating feeling began bubbling up in my gut.

"From here forward, you may refer to me by the name Sacred Elder. Your name, which is who you think you are, which you are not, I already know. Using your senses, tell me, what do you see before you?"

Before I could reply, she took a handful of ash from her tiny bag, filled her left palm, and forcefully blew the grey powdery residue at me. A gentle wind took the ash, completely covered me and lifted the rest up, filling the entire forest around us. The white-out blizzard feeling returned because I was now actually within one. Except this was not snow, it was tree ash. I could not see the Sacred Elder sitting right in front of my face, nor anything else around me for that matter.

"Don't allow your mind to deceive you. The ash was blown on you but this actually is snow. It is coming off the lake. Come, reach for my hand and let me show you."

I reached out, took her hand, and grabbed my backpack. We stood up, jumped off the stone together, and walked a few feet toward the lake. I was now able to make out her silhouette in a long white dress and also saw my feet in front of me. I wondered how it could be snowing, when it did not feel cold outside at all. In an instant, the blizzard slowed, along with time, and the flurries descended delicately upon us like soft butterfly kisses.

We came to the foot of the lake, disconnected our hands, and she once again asked me, "What do you see?"

I hesitated for a moment and then said, "I see a

frozen lake on a hot day. I do not understand how this is even possible. Before you showed up, the lake was liquid."

"That's right, there is much you and everyone else does not understand. This is due to how one's mind is programmed to believe certain things before you are even born. It is part of a passed-on generational collective consciousness reality, about which we will go into more detail soon. For now, though, just remember water has three possible states; liquid, frozen, and vapor. Notice at any given time which one your life is defined by."

We stood staring at the frozen water. The flurries completely stopped and the warmth of the sun melted the ice before our eyes. The turtles climbed back up on their rocks to thaw out and fish jumped in and out of the water. It was a wonderfully peaceful, soothing, and relaxing visual and I felt blessed to be a witness of it with my new friend.

"Remember to check in with these three states on your journey ahead to see where you are. You have the power to change your state immediately into whatever you want when you become more proficient with your ability to self-observe. Grasp the small stone in your right hand, fix your eyes upon the water, take a deep breath in and out, and gently close your eyes."

I stood there and listened to the beautiful sounds of birds singing above, turtles dropping off the rocks into the water, and the gentle whispers of the wind through the tree branches. A brisk fingertip contact struck my third-eye chakra and I opened my eyes. The Sacred Elder was gone. I felt alone for a brief moment and then the small stone in my right hand vibrated, signaling that she was close by. I put the stone in my right front pants pocket, draped my backpack over my shoulders, and walked around the right side of the lake further ahead into the deep forest.

CHAPTER SIX

THE SCARLET MACAW

The trees began to thin out and were replaced by very tall, clumpy, woody sticks of bamboo. The climate shifted dramatically into a tropical rainforest and the concert-like sounds of animals and insects were humming, thrumming, buzzing and chirping all around me.

"Where are you going?" said the voice above and to my right.

I looked over and saw no one.

"Where are you going?" came the voice again.

I looked over and this time saw a beautiful red, green, blue, and purple Scarlet Macaw perched at the top of a thick green stick of bamboo.

"I'm just walking ahead up to that clearing. Where are you going?" I replied.

I pressed on and left the bird behind me. It didn't say anything else and when I approached the vast clearing to step out of the tropical climate, I heard the parrot again.

"Your thoughts are like my speaking. Repeating the same thing over and over. Perhaps it's time to experience and think something new."

The stone in my right front pocket vibrated and sent a message through me to sit down at the tropical forest exit, which became a rocky crag. I sat a few feet before a precipice and grasped the small vibrating stone in my right hand. It became hot to the touch and began to emit a high-pitched shrill cry, which sent flocks of Scarlet Macaws scattering through the humid terrain behind me. The one who spoke stayed close-by and commented again.

"The Sacred Elder wants you to relax your right hand and release the tight grip around the stone."

I did so and the high-pitched screeching stopped.

"She also wants you to relax, close your eyes, and listen to the waters cascading down over the rocky precipice into the massive pool below."

I sat on the soft dirt, closed my eyes, and felt the thunderous sounds and vibration of the waterfall pass deeply through me. Each inhalation brought its strength into my soul and each exhalation pushed the water naturally down into the plunge pool below.

I entered into a trance-like state and my breathing intensified. Expansion and contraction of my chest cracked me open and the musical notes of the universe entered through my heart chakra. The Scarlet Macaw flew over to join me and it tapped two toes of its zygodactyl right foot at the center of my chest. The tapping continued in rhythm with the musical notes, and I lost all sense of human, and naturally settled into being. The macaw reached into my palm with its other four-toed foot, grasped the purple stone, and placed it at the opening where the musical notes entered.

The magical essence of the lavender rock bathed and nourished the universal notes, which entered and shifted the tone and vibration of the energy inside me. Joy and celebration bathed my cells and they began to dance to the rhythm of this moving world within me. An overall sense of peace, stillness, and relaxation settled in. The stone was returned to my opened right palm and the tapping stopped. I heard the delicate and graceful sounds of wings flapping away and I opened my eyes.

I took several more deep breaths and continued to

be one with the sounds of cascading rushing water. I stood up, put the rock in my right front pocket, drew my backpack over my shoulders, and heard the familiar flapping wings approaching me from behind. I did not turn around, I simply observed myself from where I stood and listened deeply.

"As you continue on, she wants you to keep your focus on the sounds of the waterfall. Do not take your attention away from that noise, even for a split second. She wants you to also recall, as needed, the feel of her fingertip contact at your third-eye chakra. Learn to open up, let go, and detach."

I nodded my head in approval, stepped to the edge of the canyon, and inhaled the waterfall's saltyish nectar aroma. Looking to my right, I observed a dense fog quickly clearing, revealing train tracks which stretched for miles in either direction. I heard the train's bellows whistling loud and clear, echoing off the escarpments before me. They beckoned me, and coupled with the stones gentle buzz in my pocket, I confidently obliged, heading off to my right to catch me some rolling black steel.

CHAPTER SEVEN

SACRED SURGERY

The muggy air intensified and my white short sleeved T-shirt was soaked. I took it off, wrung it out, and wrapped it around my head like a turban. The odor wasn't very pleasing, but at least my body felt cooler and my head had something to catch the water pouring from it.

The rocky terrain on which I was walking was lined on my left with beige sand reed grass. My strides up a steady incline became more free-flowing, care free, and the huge plunge pool below was in closer view making it incredibly inviting. I heard the voice of the Sacred Elder come through me.

"Keep your attention on each step you make. Pay even closer attention to the gap between your steps, when one foot raises and before the other touches the ground. There is stillness there. Become one with that."

I did exactly as the message instructed. Each time

I raised one foot and before the other met the ground, I entered into that open window of still presence. It felt remarkable, as how an acrobat must feel diving through a ring of fire. I was right there with each step and when I descended further down the cliffside, I noticed the rich, blue inviting pool of natural cold water close by. My thoughts became distracted and had me think of a beautiful verse from one of Rumi's love poems.

"Who could be so lucky, who comes to a lake for water and sees the reflection of moon."

I was so pulled in by the thought of the verse and the fresh cold water potentially enveloping my entire body, that I did not see the thick brown log at my next stride. It was already too late. The tip of my right sneaker found the crack between the log and rough terrain. I was flying through the air like Superman, and in slow motion I was able to observe my backpack flying beneath me.

We both crashed hard onto the ground and my backpack was much luckier. It found a clear spot to land between the thick thorny green brush, but I descended belly down on top of a conjoined fishhook cactus.

So much for keeping my attention on the gaps between my strides, I thought.

Then the pain set in, along with the familiar panic. I couldn't even move. The only saving grace about the situation I found myself in was that the hooked thorns, were lodged deep through and under my skin only from below my neck to just above my navel.

I was able to turn my face slightly to my left and realized my backpack was out of reach. I rotated my head back to center and flexed it as far as I could to assess the damage. It was hard to tell but the rotten odor emanating from beneath me through the thorn punctures was my signal that it was time to make a move. I knew it was going to be excruciating, painful and potentially fatal but I had no other choice. My only question was, "Do I go left or right?"

I mustered up some momentum, rolled my entire body to the left, and forcefully dislodged from the cactus, taking most of its hooked thorns with me.

I looked up at the heavens and with the heat of the sun penetrating through me, I began to wonder if it was my time to go. Any movement made the pain more excruciating, even each breath in and out. I yelled, writhing in agony, "I should have kept my shirt on!"

Like an upside down caterpillar, I squeezed my

abdominal muscles so they wouldn't move, bent my legs at the knees, and in an undulating wave-like motion pushed myself on my back over to my backpack. I screwed the black plastic cap off my hydroflask and poured ¾ of the water onto the open wounds where the hooked ends were protruding, and drank the rest. The oozing pus, filled with toxins and bacteria, washed away and I writhed as the pain gained in intensity.

I reached into a side pocket and took out my Swiss army knife. I opened its tweezers, and with surgical attention and precision, attempted to remove just one of the thorns to get a better idea of what I was dealing with. When I took hold of the curved hook and pulled, it wouldn't budge or release from my skin. It would resist and strengthen its hold deep through my skin and within muscle.

I took hold of another hook and then another but to no avail. I put the tweezers back into the slot of the red knife, placed it back into my backpack, and put the sack underneath my sweaty and stiff neck for support. After a few more minutes of lying there unable to move, and with my thoughts racing, the powerful sun beat harder, dehydration set in, and I lost *most* of my consciousness. My eyes remained slightly open and vision became blurred and fogged at best.

In this groggy hazed state, I heard the high-pitched screeching of the Scarlet Macaw approaching. I felt its flapping wings above my head, which created a nice cool breeze against my wet skin. I took a deep breath in and out and felt my body ease its resistance. Six inches above my eyes, I saw the outlines of what appeared to be three monarch butterflies gently hovering. The larger one in the middle slowly descended, landed at the center of my forehead between my eyes, and began to speak.

"As the great Buddha said, 'Form is emptiness and emptiness is form.' What you were told earlier about the space between your steps, now it is time for you to take it a step further and get in touch with the gaps between your thoughts. Right now, observe yourself and become aware of the space that exists between each thought. Connect with that deep presence and make this spatial awareness your current meditation while the sacred surgical performance is done through you. Remember, your entire life is a meditation when you are awake for it."

I felt the monarchs two navigational antennae connect with and open my third-eye chakra. She then attached her two front legs to my spirit within the crown chakra, lifted it out from my body, and flew it three feet above my physical shell to the Scarlet Macaw. The bird grasped it with its K-like foot formation, the butterfly flew back down to my crown chakra, and her two assistants came to my right front pants pocket to retrieve the small purple stone.

I hovered above in spirit and looked down as my machine was being worked on by three winged magicians. The butterfly who removed the stone carried it above my belly button and released it. The stone remained suspended in the air like a tiny purple balloon an inch above my abdomen. The butterfly at my crown chakra flew to the stone and brought all four of its legs swiftly through the air in a crisscrossed pattern, the way a conductor joyfully leads a harmonic symphony. The stone split into seven equal discs, which the three butterflies grabbed simultaneously and like mini purple Frisbees, they curled the ends of their legs and tossed each one at my seven chakra points.

The Scarlet Macaw descended two feet and hovered above my head. It continued to hold my spirit in one foot, which left the other one free. The three butterflies separated themselves equidistant between the 7 chakras and the spinning purple discs, hovering an inch directly above them. The Scarlet Macaw let out a loud shrill and with his free foot, shot a sustained bolt of white lightning from it, piercing directly through the disc and into my crown chakra.

This electrical discharge passed through my body in a straight line beginning at the top of my head all the way to the region of my lower pelvis and opened the six remaining chakras. The butterflies pointed their two front legs at the center of discs two, four, and six and shot electricity bolts through them. The butterfly hovering at the abdomen and the one hovering in the pelvic region shot electric bolts through spinning discs five and seven. Now, with all seven purple discs fully charged, they began to feverishly spin in a counter-clockwise direction and took on the color of their respective chakra. I observed from top to bottom, violet, indigo, blue, green, yellow, orange, and red shooting up through my body like beams of parallel light.

My body began to shake and vibrate like a race car revving before the start of a race. The discs spun faster and the hooked thorns within my muscles and skin twisted like corkscrews and slowly unhinged from my body. Exiting my skin, they made a popping sound and flew out like champagne corks. Pop, pop, pop, one after the other until they were all removed. The sacred surgical procedure finished, as did the tiny lightning bolts from the butterfly legs.

The Scarlet Macaw let out a final piercing cry, the sustained electrical bolt from his foot stopped, and he kept my spirit locked firmly in the tight grasp of his four toes.

The butterflies at the top and bottom flew to disc one and seven respectively. They turned them up to face one another at each end and spun them several times until they rotated at warp speed. This initiated the other five discs to spin at a similar speed, tone, and vibration while still facing parallel above its associated chakra.

Tiny rivers of blue and green pus began to flow out of every hole the thorns left behind. It took several minutes for it to drain out because I was on my back. My entire torso was covered and there was a one-and-a-half-inch thick pool built up on each side where my body met the soft pebbly ground. Lucky for me, I was out of my body, because if I were in it I most definitely would have thrown up from the sights, popping sounds, and odiferous liquids.

The butterflies closest to the top and bottom gathered the spinning discs at either end and slowly brought them toward each other, connecting each disc as though they were apple slices forming back into its original solid state. The butterfly in the center took the solidified purple rock from its associates, flew the stone quickly over each hole, while the other butterflies, the Scarlet Macaw, and my spirit, watched them begin to close.

The Mystical Macaw said to me, "I am going to return the formless part of you, your being essence, back into your physical form, the human part of you. Get in touch with the duality of these two as your body heals. Your formless essence must initiate a deep body fever at once, to push all remaining bacteria and toxicity from deep within you."

He lowered me down into my crown chakra and perched himself at the top of my head. The butterflies joined him and the four bent at their knees as if praying a special and sacred healing prayer. The Macaw jumped off and flew over to rest on a large brown boulder to my right while the butterflies took off and circled a few feet above me. They watched and waited while my body began to heat up and pour out beads of sweat.

The butterfly holding the purple stone brought it back to my right front pocket and one of the other butterflies tucked it in with its legs. They found the leather pouch in my backpack, worked together to untie its strings, and removed some of the grey flaky ash at the bottom with their tongues.

The sweat was really pouring out now. So much so, that it mixed with the pus and dirt where my skin met the ground and began flowing in the direction of the massive plunge pool to my right. What I'd give to be in that blue frigid water right now! I could smell the sweet aroma coming off the water and floating in the air toward me.

The two butterflies, with the ash in their straw-like tongues, flew over to meet the third one at my third-eye chakra. They spit the ash through their tongues between my eyes which stuck to my skin like glue. The third butterfly gently began rubbing the oatmeal material into my skin with her front legs. The fever began to break and the trio flew off and landed close by on yellow daisies to drink nectar and monitor me.

After several minutes, I felt energy returning to my body but I was still too weak to walk. I sat up, palms at my sides, my legs outstretched. I yelled out to the Scarlet Macaw and butterflies a hearty and thunderous, "Thank you!" They knew their work here was mostly done and began to fly back up the incline of the mountain, turning back to look at me every minute or so until I was unable to see them any longer.

CHAPTER EIGHT

CHAMPO AND EINSTEIN

I heard the sounds of a broad, sharp blade swiftly slashing through the thick hanging vines, tall reeds, and shrubbery behind me. I was still too weak to walk but was now able to turn my body and see what was coming toward me. Whoever was approaching was still behind the veil of natural bush, so I grabbed my Swiss Army Knife and produced the only sharp blade it possessed. It was quite comical and the little laughter it produced felt good after the horrible pain I had just experienced.

Realizing the small knife was no match for the machete I was listening to, I threw it back into the backpack, zipped it up, and rested my head back down on top of it. The foliage ripping behind me intensified and I closed my eyes. Maybe they'd stumble upon me and think I was dead or at least sleeping and therefore not a threat.

The footsteps crunched the earth by my ears and I didn't move a muscle. I heard and felt their breath in front of my face, while their index and middle fingers touched the right side of my neck, checking for signs of pulsating carotid arterial life. They definitely found some, although I kept my eyes closed hoping they'd think I had passed out after viewing the multiple holes on my torso and the blue-green pus mixed with sweat on the ground beside me.

A man picked me up, curled me over his left shoulder, and carried me back along the path he had cleared. With my head and face hitting his back on each stride, I opened my eyes and saw the tiny legs of a man whom I felt was very gentle and kindhearted. He whistled Beethoven's Ninth in perfect pitch and tone with a beautiful background of multiple frogs, cicadas, and monkeys joining in. Every few steps he stopped the whistle and mumbled the words, "Must hurry," under his breath.

The music out of his mouth coupled with the meditative steps helped me drift off to sleep. I wasn't certain how long I was passed out over his shoulder but when I came to, I found myself lying on my back on a large oak, wood-stained antique examination table. It was hard and uncomfortable but much better than the conditions I had just come from. I heard his whistling continue off by the plunge pool outside the hut I found myself in and tried to prop myself up but couldn't move. I bent my head forward, saw I was covered in thick ashy paste, and tightly wrapped in multiple human-sized Coccoloba gigantifolia leaves.

The massive leaves smelled like rotting human feet. I had to hold my breath from the strong odor and then closed off my olfactory sense and gently breathed in and out through my mouth. The large hut I found myself in was constructed out of massive green bamboo stalks from the humid forest above. They made up the entirety of the edifice, including walls, ceiling, and flooring. The floor was especially special in that its unique appearance comprised of stripped-down shredded fiber strands woven together in a zig-zag pattern, compressed, and lightly stained.

The whistling got louder as his footsteps approached the hut from the plunge pool outside. I turned my face to the right and he entered the room. A confident aura surrounded the man and he began to speak.

"My Scarlet Macaw, whose name is Einstein, and the three butterflies, saved your life. Now I am going to bring you fully back to it. The blue and green pus your body generated was an innate defense mechanism to ward off the hooked thorns that lodged deep in your body. The thorns themselves are not toxic but the holes they created can become infected quite rapidly. The ancient and sacred surgery performed on you prevented early-onset infection, yet there is still much prevention and healing left to do."

"Thank you for everything that you and Einstein are doing for me. I feel very lucky to be alive," I replied.

"Luck has very little to do with it. It is no accident you stumbled upon this dimension. My name is Champo and from the tag on your backpack, you are David. Well, that's the name you were given by your parents at birth. Who you are is something else entirely."

Champo walked over to me and checked under the heavy wrappings of green smelly leaves. He poured warm water between certain layers and sprinkled in more of the ash. He wrapped the leaves back around me and skillfully tied small green bamboo strands around the foliage.

"You must do the rest of the healing with your mind. Lay back and rest, visualizing yourself already fully healed. The ash paste and Coccoloba gigantifolia leaves will aid you in the process. Focus all of your attention on the present moment. That is where healing occurs. No healing takes place in the past or the future."

He walked away from the table whistling Mozart's *Magic Flute* with precision and perfection. The notes sounded beautiful and I felt their vibration beneath the leaves wrapped around me. Einstein flew into the hut and landed high up in a custom made bamboo tree stand. I watched as he moved from branch to branch with ease, wrapping his feet around the naturally distinctive curves. "Thank you Einstein," I called out.

"You are very welcome. The Sacred Elder has another message for you. She wants you to quiet your mind and become very still internally. Close your eyes and bring your attention to each puncture wound. At each hole, imagine the essence of love seeping in and bathing it with its light and healing wisdom. Go from one hole to the next, making this your meditation practice for now."

I closed my eyes and went from hole to hole, bringing a pinkish hue to it. I became the loving energy itself, filling each puncture with the universal essence of healing. I now understood what the saying "Love heals," meant. Lying on this table and visualizing myself healed made me realize my accident happened to teach me a lesson. I am here now in this beautiful hut, with this amazing man and bird, to learn how to heal and love myself from within in order to bring that message out for others.

Frigid ice water forcefully landed on my face, taking me out of my zone. I opened my mouth to breathe and the water came rushing in. I swallowed loads of it and it felt, smelled, and tasted refreshing.

"Drink more, David," said Champo.

"This water has remarkable natural healing properties straight out of the waterfall. It has tiny green algae microorganisms that will both sustain and boost your immune system. Plus, you need to rehydrate, having lost much water through sweating in the jungle. Replenish the fluids and foods of your body, mind, soul, and spirit. Close your eyes, scan the puncture wounds, and focus your energy inward, on the repairing of your cells."

I felt more liquid on my face and drank it in. The ice-cold feeling flowed over and through the leaves I was encased within and my entire body began to tingle and feel numb. I sense the holes healing up completely and felt the ashy paste popping out of them. As more plunge-pool water was traversing through the spaces between the leaves, I felt the ash wash from my body and spill onto the bamboo floor. The odor of that combination was now too much and I turned my face to the right and rid my body of any remaining toxins.

Champo said, "Very good. Release all of it, through many orifices."

We both laughed and then Einstein joined in, which made me and Champo laugh even harder.

"Laughter is the best medicine," said Champo and Einstein mimicked him.

"Laughter is the best medicine, awk, laughter is the best medicine."

Champo poured another plume of water over me and it felt magnificent. The leaves were drenched and the bamboo string ties came undone by themselves. He unwrapped me, threw the stinky leaves into a large wooden barrel, picked up a small barber's neck brush and swept the remining paste off of my skin. One last dousing of clear frigid water took the remaining paste off me.

"Fever completely gone and no infection. You healed yourself," he said.

I had a tremendous amount of newfound energy and felt amazing. Champo placed large hot, moist, white towels over the front of my body and the only part of me not covered was my face.

"One more round of ice water coming right up. Hot and cold combination invigorating for mind and body. Then I have special surprise for you."

The towels felt incredibly hot on my skin and I was afraid they were burning me. I took the one under my chin and began to remove it when he said, "No, no, don't touch. Final healing technique." He tucked the towel back down and ice water came over them, drenching me from head to toe. An additional surge of energy mustered up through me and quite frankly I didn't realize I could garner more.

"Before you get up off the table, take a look at Einstein up there on bamboo perch. You think his name is Einstein, which makes you think of the person. That is your mind deceiving you. What is Einstein? Is he a bird? No! Be cautious of the names and labels placed on things. They lose their essence entirely because of them."

He gently pulled on a rope attached to the table, which brought the section under my head to my low-back up 45 degrees. He pulled another rope attached to the table, which brought the section from my butt to my feet downward on another 45 degree angle. I slid off the table, landed perfectly on my feet, and the soaked towels fell off me onto the floor. I was embarrassed standing there in my birthday suit, when Champo looked to his right and said, "Follow me."

We walked out of the hut and into the bright sunshine. It felt great having the rays of the sun on my bare skin. I couldn't recall the last time I tanned completely nude or skinny-dipped, for that matter. The sandy terrain under my bare feet made me feel like I was at the beach. We came up to the edge of the massive natural plunge-pool and I was finally going to have my wish from earlier today come true.

Champo took off everything except for his white boxer shorts, yelled "Kowabunga," and cannonballed into the water. He let out a loud "Woowee," and I joined him by diving head first into the frigid pool.

"Feels incredible, woowee!" I exclaimed.

"Champo, I do not remember the last time I was

on vacation and at such a beautiful place. I truly cannot recall when the last time was that I just simply let-go and surrendered."

"You are good as new, David. Maybe even better than before. It is good you feel like you are on vacation and letting go. You must consider your life and ask yourself if you enjoy the work you do or if you feel as though you have to vacate from it. For now, enjoy the natural cold plunge in my backyard!"

We swam, splashed, laughed, and took in the beauty of the rock, clear water, and the magnificent blue sky above. "Nature provides all the clues we need to live a happy and joyous life. It is all right in front of us all the time. All we have to do is look for it."

He was right, I felt as though I was a slave to my store and my passion for it has escaped me. I am vacating it and also attending multiple personal-growth seminars to rediscover my purpose and passion. I know that I must make a shift, heal the inner part of me, and rekindle my excitement and zest for life. The accident I just healed from was no accident. It was a signpost pointing me in the direction I must now travel.

"Your smelly and dirty clothing is now clean and

dry. I washed it in here while you were meditating on the table. They are over there on the rocks, nice and hot for you to get dressed in now. Clean towel next to them to dry off. Meet me back in the hut for hot food and tea."

I had an overwhelming sense of gratitude for Champo and didn't know how I could ever repay him. I knew I had to, though, and that the opportunity would present itself at just the right time. I dried off, got dressed, and headed back toward the hut.

Inspecting it from the outside for the first time, I noticed the intricate vernacular architecture used to erect the building. I observed mud, leaves, animal hides, straw, and large rocks all nestled within and between the large bamboo logs. The most identifying and unusual feature was the windcatcher, or wind tower just to the left of the main entrance, which Champo used to create natural ventilation and passive cooling in the hut.

"How can I ever repay you Champo?" I asked, entering the hut.

"By coming over and joining me for an early dinner. Come sit down and take a load off. You must refuel before heading to catch the train!"

I had completely forgotten about the train. I had

my sights on catching it earlier and realized that when one is in the present moment, nothing is happening except what is directly in front of them.

"Tell me what you were just thinking right now," said Champo.

He put some white rice in a small steel cup, walked over, and reached up to rest it on a wood slab for Einstein.

"Well, I was considering earlier today when my focus was on tracking down a black train I saw when I was at the top of the mountain. My attention was on what was next and ahead of me versus paying complete attention to the present moment."

"Let's dig in and refuel our cells, shall we?" asked Champo.

He handed me a serving spoon and gestured for me to begin. I couldn't and turned the handle of the wooden spook towards him. He grasped it and took some of the hot steamy rice onto his bamboo plate. I wondered how and when he found the time to prepare this rich, colorful, and delectable smorgasbord. There were noodles with vegetables, a separate bowl with tofu, a red potato soup, and green curry in a hot pot.

Champo pulled two pair of exquisitely handcrafted wooden chopsticks from under the table. They were both adorned with beautiful carvings of dragons and lotus flowers and were finished off with a smooth clear varnish.

He handed me a pair and said, "We will eat in style with these. But I want you to eat with your non-dominant hand. Useful exercise for your concentration, frustration, and your neurology. They are also a gift to you from me."

I took the wooden masterpieces and simply brought them elongated vertically between the grasp of my palms and bowed to him in gratitude several times.

Champo ate quickly and I was going very slow. The unusual feeling of eating with my left hand coupled with my stomach still feeling a bit off, made for a gradual eating experience. I consumed mostly rice with some potato chunks from the soup and Bok Choy. This gave him some time to slowly sip hot green tea and stare in my direction.

He was contemplating his upcoming words meticulously and then said, "How do you enjoy my cooking?" and brought a bright wide smile to his face.

"I love it. I still don't know how you found the time or how I can ever repay you."

"No need to focus on repaying me. This is how friends show up for one another. The most you can do for me is find yourself through additional healing. You mentioned distraction and the present moment before we started to eat. Most people are living their present moment as a projection of their past, which resides in their future, and thus not allowing anything new into their life.

"Remember the lake you sat at with the Sacred Elder earlier today? Ponder on the lake as you make your journey to the train and consider if you are fluid-like and going with the flow of life. If you are not, then you will be breathing very shallow and either living in a solid and frozen past or disconnected and disassociated in your vapor-like future."

I took the last couple of bites of rice and potato chunks and drank soup broth, while Champo cleared the table, washed the wood bamboo dishes, and packed a few containers for me to take. We spent the next several minutes in silence and grateful reflection.

I stood up and brought my dish and chopsticks to the washing basin. "You leave those for me," Champo said.

I handed them over and he placed them on the wood counter next to the sink. I unzipped my backpack, loaded the food inside, zipped it up, and put it across my back. Champo placed the beautiful chopsticks into a long side pocket of the pack and we hugged, bidding each other farewell.

"David this is not good-bye, it is until we meet again, which I sense will be very soon."

"Very soon," came from Einstein and we both laughed.

"Einstein will see you very soon, too."

"I do hope so, Champo. You have been a life-saver and amazing friend. Good-bye, Einstein."

"Very soon," came again from Einstein.

At the front door, I put my hands together in front of my chest and bowed at Champo and Einstein. Champo did the same and Einstein was bouncing up and down on his wood perch.

"Like this empty tea cup I am holding, you must empty your cup when you enter the train."

I bowed once more, walked backward out of the hut, and out into the thick brush alongside the plunge-pool.

CHAPTER NINE

THE MORCUBI

The train's whistle blew loud and I headed straight for it between the two gigantic red boulders up ahead. I heard Champo's voice yelling from far behind me, "You healed up body very good but still have heavy heart to heal. You come back and visit Champo soon! We eat leftovers! Hurry, the train is calling ... for you."

The light was slowly escaping from the sky and I picked up my pace to catch the train before sundown. The terrain continued its decline and was made up of a pleasantly coarse narrow path below my feet. The two huge rocky cliffs on either side of me formed a mountain crevasse similar to Kjeragbolten in Norway. All of the heavy thick bush, brush, and greenery from before evaporated and all that remained were sparse disbursements of tall willow shrubs and beige beach grass. Small flocks of brown and white Rock Ptarmigans flew high above and called out a quiet, clucking kuk-kuk-kuk in unison.

I made sure to glance at them rather quickly and keep my eyes firmly planted where my next steps were going to be. The train was more visible and rested just five football fields straight ahead. Or so I thought. My increasing concern was on the steadily descending topography. What initially appeared to be a level grade to the train, had turned into a future rock-climbing descent similar to China's White Mountain. I just didn't have the appropriate gear with me.

I approached the massive flat rock now directly in front of me, and saw three summits: to my left, right, and facing me of approximately 5,000 feet each. Turning back and walking back up from where I came was not an option, so I sat for a moment up against the white crag and considered my situation.

The small purple stone in my right front pocket began to vibrate and I removed it. I crossed my legs, opened my palms, and rested them facing upward on my knees. The stone became warm in the center of my right palm and continued to buzz. I felt an intuitive nudging to turn my body around 180° and face the white stone slab. With the dimmed lighting at this depth of the canyon and the man-made screen before me, the small stone emitted a projection beam at the backdrop.

The image of the Sacred Elder, dressed in her long white gown, illuminated brightly on the white rock screen to deliver a mystical holographic message.

"You are at an interesting and critical impasse. You have learned enough up to now to turn back and return from where you originated. Or, you continue forward and experience things you never could have imagined with your current mental state. If you choose to continue forward, after this message disappears, turn the stone that rests in your palm with the index finger and thumb of your left hand ¼ counterclockwise. And make sure your backpack straps are tight around your shoulders."

The holoprojected image evaporated and I took a long swig of fresh air deep into my lungs. I held it in there, turned the stone ¼ counterclockwise, and forced the air out fully through my mouth. I tightened the black nylon straps around my shoulders and while doing so, detected a monstrous blackening hovering over me, which cast a magnificent shadow on the white wall. I put the stone back in my front pocket and bent my neck backward to look up.

I wasn't sure if what hovered twenty feet above me was a four-blade, twin-engine, Blackhawk helicopter or a four-winged dragon. I was hoping for the former and would have enjoyed neither. It confirmed it was the latter when its large mouth opened and the huge frame swooped down and wrapped its massive front incisors around the top carry handle of my black and grey ultra-nylon rucksack.

I would have resisted, flailed, passed out, or all three, if not for the Sacred Elder's recent message. The beast flapped its four thick-skinned wings, slowly raising us into the chilled thin air. It stopped at the first of three deep ledges embedded into the mountain, and descended me down, onto my feet. The winged animal flew off and settled into a circular formation between the high stone walls that connected to the one I was standing on. It darted toward me and positioned itself at the edge of the ledge, bringing its large right grey-blue eyeball over to my face.

"The Sacred Elder sent me to give you a lift up to the train. Before I take you up, however, how would you like to climb on my back and go for a ride? It's amazing what you can see from various angles high-up over the rocky crags."

"Sure, I'd love to go."

"Just grab a hold of the rope that extends over my back at the neck and climb up. You won't hurt me by digging your heels into my thick skin."

I took hold of the hairy and somewhat moist rope-like apparatus and yanked on it while climbing up its scarred and scaley reptilian hide. The grooves in the scales made perfect inserts for my shoes, as I climbed. I was positioned close to its neck and centered. As I held tightly onto the slimy rope, we took off and ascended toward the humid forest.

My balance was completely off, which prevented me from enjoying the majestic waterfall, plunge-pool, and other forest attractions. Then the beast spoke but the strange thing was that its mouth remained closed. I thought perhaps I was hallucinating, or possibly the higher altitude coupled with the immediate motion sickness was affecting me.

"How am I hearing you?" I asked.

"First off, let's do a proper introduction. My name

is Sampson, the Sacred Elder's personal travel assistant. And you are David, correct?"

"Yes. Hi, Sampson, that is correct. My name is David. It's a pleasure to meet you. Again, your mouth was just closed. How am I hearing your words?"

"They are not actually words as you think of words conceptually. I am speaking to you through a different mechanism entirely. Keep holding the rope and listen. Actually it is not a rope, it is part of my body. Part of a network system that you refer to as neurology."

"Okay, I get it. So your brain is communicating through this thing I'm holding which is actually part of your neural network. What we have on the inside only, part of yours is on the outside."

"You are correct," said Sampson.

I started getting the hang of the balancing act on top of Sampson, looked over to my left and saw Champo waving to us with Einstein on his left shoulder bouncing up and down and screaming out, "Very soon!"

I held the rope with my left hand, waved to them with my right hand, and called out, "Hey you two! Look at me."

I temporarily lost my balance and quickly grabbed

the rope with both hands and maneuvered body positions. I heard Einstein call out, "What a klutz, baak, what a klutz," as we drifted higher into the chilled mist of the vast waterfall.

The slimy rope buzzed and Sampson spoke through it, "Einstein is an old, funny friend. He is the ancient companion of the mystic Champo. Champo and the Sacred Elder have been friends for many centuries. The sense I am getting from your energy is that you will be next in line to join the sacred team. First things first. I am going to shut my rope so you can take in the sights before I bring you back to the next ledge where the train resides."

I saw the spot where Champo threw me over his shoulder earlier, the massive plunge-pool with its clear frigid water, the majestic waterfall, and the vast valley between the two massive brown rock mountains. Sampson took a quick, sharp, angled turn to the left and ascended very high. I closed my eyes and breathed in the rich fine air. When he leveled off, I opened my eyes and observed the bamboo, Hyperion trees, liquified lake, large round rocks, stone paver path, and the small stone home.

The rope buzzed and Sampson said, "It's me again. Sometimes it is useful to see where you have been in order to know where you are heading. Using your senses, take an impression of all you see without giving the things the customary name. Just observe down there and allow it to make their impression within you. This is one of the gateways into the present moment. Be with the trees, lake, waterfall, plunge-pool, and mountain ranges without naming them. How does their essence feel?"

I practiced this as we slowly glided above the forest and contemplated how all things we come to know are given names, which has that thing completely lose its essence. This must mean we never truly know the thing at all. We stop ourselves from knowing it when we name it. I tested this out by asking Sampson a question.

"Sampson, can you fly me to the top of the water-fall please? I'd like to come face to face with what we know of as a tree."

"Coming right up!"

We shot to the top of the waterfall and hovered over the piney wood perfumed evergreen trees that stuck out of the water. The refreshing scent was wonderful and even produced multiple deep sighs from Sampson. I brushed my left foot over the thick leathery needle-like green leaves and became engrossed by its essence, versus what the thing was called. It produced a different experience entirely, where I found myself engaged with the stillness of the present moment instead of being taken by the strong currents of my useless runaway thoughts.

"Now you are there. I sense it through the rope. Take this stillness of the present moment with you as we glide back down through the crevasse to the second tiered ledge in the mountain. There is much you will learn by being friends with the present moment. When you are here, now, thoughts subside and the rapture of 'isness' ensues. Simply observe and try not to call the thing you see by the name it was given."

We glided back down toward the mountain with ledges and I observed Sampson's four wings. I did not think of the name wing while looking at them. Instead, I watched to my right, as two thick bony structures with curved ends flapped in opposite directions of one another. The wing above flapped down and clockwise and the wing below flapped up and counterclockwise.

It was stunning to observe. On my left, the wings did the exact opposite of what the wings on Sampson's right performed.

He flew in from off to the left expanse and when we closed in on the ledge, Sampson answered my original question.

"My species, the Morcubi, has an ancient communication system that was utilized by your people eons ago. What you once referred to as Mental Telepathy we call Binocule Communication. Remember to not be focused on what it is called. Be aware of what it's capable of. We communicate through vibrational energetic airwaves with our kind and when one of your types sits on us and holds the rope, we reignite the ancient communication system within them. This is how you are hearing me now."

It was a fascinating explanation and communication experience. The trip around the valley and forest was incredible, as well. Seeing, hearing, smelling, feeling, and tasting all that was below, left me in a wonderful state of gratitude and the notion of just how very fortunate I was to simply be alive.

We arrived back at the great white stone wall and

Sampson landed on the second ledge of three. The ridge was much wider than the one below and above and was situated behind a small white brick building with a green ceramic tiled roof.

"This is where you get off to catch the train, David. Enter the white building through the black rear entrance door and there you will find your ticket to ride."

Before I let go of the rope to slide off Sampson, I noticed the same three butterflies who performed surgery on me earlier. They flew alongside the left side of his large leathery and weathered face. They drifted at his left ear and the four of them entered into lengthy conversation. It was unique, watching them communicate; Sampson gesturing with his head movements and tongue, and the butterflies with their wing, antennae, and leg engagements.

When the conversation was finished, the two orange and black Monarchs on the ends flew up to rest on either of Sampson's white horns at the top of his head, while the butterfly in the middle flew over and hovered before my face. She brought her antennae to my third eye and opened it widely.

"You have healed your physical body well, thanks

to your inner healing recuperative powers, our sacred surgical procedures, Einstein's brilliance, and Champo's grace. There is still a residual inner emotional and spiritual healing from your past that must occur in order for you to realize and actualize your true life purpose and aim. This will happen on the magical and mystical train ride if you choose to climb aboard."

The Monarch detached from my third-eye chakra, flew down to the purple stone inside my front pocket, and landed on top of it. A light buzz came from the stone, shot through my pants into the butterfly, and changed her colors from orange and black to lavender and white. The buzzing stopped and the butterfly, in her new colors, flew off and hovered between the white-brick building and the cliff's ledge.

I thanked Sampson, let go of the slimy rope and leaned forward to give him a hug around his rough scaly neck. From this position, I rolled off the left side of him and both feet landed on the pebbly dirt ridge. As I turned to walk toward and enter the small white brick building, I felt something hit and attach to the temple on the right side of my face. I turned quickly while reaching up to see what it was and to my surprise,

Sampson had disconnected his neural rope apparatus at its mid-point and connected it to me.

I was frozen in place, not able to move forward, back, left or right. Through the thick, slimy, and wiry black rope, Sampson sent two slightly different sound frequencies into each ear. These binaural beats soothed and calmed me, while sending an exacting message into the core of my brain of what I was to do next.

"The wire will disconnect from your temple. Then, remove the purple stone from your right front pants pocket and hold it ½ inch above the purple and white butterfly. When she told you before that you have the choice whether to climb aboard the train or not, after you do this with the stone, you'll see that climbing aboard is your only option. Travel well and we will connect again soon."

The slimy black thick wire at my right temple released, producing a loud suction pop. It was nice to be able to move again. Feeling free, I reached into my pocket with my right hand and lifted the stone ½ inch above the butterfly, who rested six feet in the air.

CHAPTER TEN

THE BROWN BEAST

During her lifetime she had already transformed herself from a crawling hairy bright yellow, black, and clear, clean white caterpillar into an orange-and-black winged specimen. She then morphed colors to purple and white and now, under the transformative rain-showering white glow projecting down off the mystical stone, the Sacred Elder emerged from the butterfly in a long white gown. Her white hair had subtle purple highlights and the leather pouch containing sacred ash was tied around her waist.

The light traced back up into the stone, I put it back in my pocket, and the Sacred Elder said, "Let's go! We have a brown train to catch."

We waved good-bye to Sampson, to the other two Monarchs, and made a beeline to the back door of the small white ticket building. The Sacred Eder didn't say anything else to me. Not a word about how she appeared out of a butterfly. I sensed there might be something stated about it on the locomotive.

We walked through the black back door of the white building; the small structure was musty and the walls looked cold and wet. The creamy orange one-inch ceramic mosaic floor tiles had a honeycomb geometric shape pattern accented by a simple solid black border where the tiles met the wood ticket windows. Weeds sporadically protruded out from the grout lines where grout no longer resided and the old green painted benches were naked, worn down to their original grey timber surfaces.

The ticket windows were boarded up with old, mildewy plywood. The thin sheets, which once created the impression of one piece of wood, revealed their weaknesses. Each glued layer was separated, fanned out, cracked, and weathered by time.

I walked up to one of the boarded windows, pried the old wood away, and noticed an old roll of train tickets resting on the ancient green marble counter behind the window. I reached my arm through the small opening at the base of the window and tore two red tickets off the dank roll.

I handed one to the Sacred Elder and we quickly exited out the front door. I stopped dead in my tracks a few feet in front of the old building and marveled at the massive cast-iron shiny brown train before me. This unassuming monster rested gently on the shiny steel alloy tracks beneath it. Between the tracks were heavy loads of crushed limestone railroad ballast, appearing to hold the wooden cross ties, and in turn the rails, in place.

Each of the five shiny brown cars stood ten feet tall, including the caboose. They had old worn peeling capitalized gold lettering on the sides. The only thing legible was the big bright word **FIVE** smack on the front of the nose of the train and the letters **TRANS** immediately under it. I figured those letters had something to do with the Transportation Line the train was affiliated with.

"All aboard!" came the voice over the loudspeakers from inside the train and from the one small box speaker on the tall Pullman brown platform pole behind me.

The Sacred Elder turned and said, "Well, are we just going to stand here all day? Let's get a move on and board this shiny beast!"

The door of the first car opened and the Sacred

Elder went up the three small black metal steps first; I quickly followed. The inside of the car was magnificent. Cuban mahogany lined the walls along with brass light fixtures, zinc railings, rich upholstered seats, and floral patterned carpet. I took an impression of the amazing details and sat down in the front row at the left window.

The Sacred Elder said, "This is an old Pullman Classic. Did you get a good look at the deep chocolate brown paint on the outside body? Look up and see the same color painted on cast-iron ceiling box panels trimmed out by the Cuban mahogany. Just brilliant."

"I have never seen anything like it before. It *is* brilliant." I replied.

"David, we are on this train for you to go through your own transformation process and complete whatever is incomplete inside of you. One could say that the caterpillar is incomplete, having the promise of the butterfly within it. One could also say that humans have not learned how to be and therefore have the promise of transforming into their true essence, too. They must first remember the possibility and in order for you to do so, we will ride together through five mystical tunnels!"

I found what she was saying rather intriguing and

asked, "Well, what does all of this have to do with me specifically?"

"Specifically, nothing and everything. It has to do with you and the entire collective of humanity being asleep and having the promise of awakening within.

"When you take a piece of wood from a fallen tree and put it into a fire, the wood changes its form into ash. The tree-ness is still in there, just being expressed in a different form. The human being has the same potential within to change its form and awaken into something new. People stay stuck in limited thinking and belief systems and therefore do not grow. They must remember who they came here to be and open themselves up to transforming into something new. You will eventually help in their process David."

She stopped speaking and looked out of the magnificently clear window at the front of the car. The rear mahogany door slowly creaked open, I turned and was incredibly surprised to see Einstein perched on Champo's right shoulder.

Champo was dressed in an old traditional conductor's uniform; a three-piece suit made up of a coat, vest, and trousers. Pockets were of the slit type, no flaps, and were edged with browned leather, as were his coat cuffs. His navy-blue, single-breasted coat was four-button and had two-sided pockets on each side, arranged one above the other. The vest appeared to also have several pockets, although they didn't have the leather treatment on the pocket edges like the main coat. His hat was a military-style pillbox with a brim.

A loud "Very soon," came from Einstein as he excitedly bounced up and down.

I got up and ran over to Champo to give him a hug and then scratched Einstein's crest of blue feathers at the top of his head.

"Good to see you, David," said Champo.

"Great to see the both of you," I replied.

The Sacred Elder and Champo embraced. It felt amazing to be on this beautiful train with good friends. I took my seat and the Sacred Elder sat in the same row at the opposing window.

Champo said, "Perch," and Einstein flew off his shoulder and up to a beautifully bamboo crafted and curved ledge at the chocolate brown ceiling. He closed the wooden door to Car One behind him, which initiated a transformation at the car's dashboard controls.

Champo walked over to the futuristic controls, turned to me and said, "At a certain point in life, one will have a choice. You can either get really real about areas you have been living inauthentically or continue on living the life of a lie. If you are ready to play full-out and are sincerely committed to your aim of personal growth and transformation, we will begin this sacred journey through the Five Tunnels of Avalon."

CHAPTER ELEVEN

FORGIVENESS

The Sacred Elder looked to her left at me and I looked at Champo, "Let's go!"

"Very well then. A few housekeeping items before we depart Station 1. There is no smoking, gum chewing, or swearing on this train. There's also no eating, drinking, or horseplay of any kind. If you fail to comply with these rules, you will have to get off at the next stop. Now then, looking over at the white brick building at your left, you will see in large capitalized black letters the word **FORGIVENESS.** That is symbolic of the first tunnel we will pass through as well as a necessity to experience a fulfilled life."

I looked at the small white brick ticket building and wondered how I failed to notice the word **FORGIVENESS** there before. I was either too distracted by the beautiful chocolate brown train before me or those letters magically appeared when Champo closed the rear door of Car One. Nevertheless, here they were and I had absolutely no idea what was in store for me.

"Remember David, it is useful for you to be okay not knowing."

The Sacred Elder's words rang true. I always wanted to know what was next up in my life and was barely present to the now. Here was my chance to let go and have this brown beast do what it was going to do.

Champo asked us both to approach the futuristic dashboard. We rose out of our comfortable green and brown plaid fabric chairs and met Champo there. A shiny brushed-nickel throttle sat to the right of five illuminated colored square buttons. Two horizontal rectangular windows met a vertical window at the center of the front wall. Several other buttons adorned the dash with symbols and characters that were foreign to me.

"May I have your tickets please?"

The Sacred Elder and I handed Champo our red tickets.

"No. You each take your own ticket and put it at the entrance to this slot at the dashboard."

The Sacred Elder fed hers in first and a sucking noise confirmed it was fully drawn in. I supplied my red ticket into the slot next and the same sucking sound occurred.

"Take your seats immediately and grasp the wood handles outside your knees tightly with your right and left hands," Champo said.

We both quickly sat down and grabbed the Cuban mahogany wood handles on either side of our knees; the inside of the train went pitch black.

A white button on the dashboard flashed, Champo depressed it, and called out, "And in 3, 2, 1" the train rose three inches off the tracks and the inside of the car became illuminated in a futuristic soft amber LED light from above.

"As you can see out of the windows before you, there resides a tunnel in front of us. This tunnel represents the tunnel of Forgiveness and is the first of five sacred tunnels we will pass through. Pass through is not quite the appropriate terminology, although it does it enough justice for now. You will understand what I am referring to in the experience within the tunnel. David, please come join me."

I went to join Champo at the dashboard which included the five colored square buttons, the speed control lever, and the other buttons with symbols on them I did not recognize. My sense was those buttons gave the person who depressed them the ability to move a model on the three windows (screens) in front of us by shifting their hands in the air.

Champo flipped up the clear plastic cover revealing the colored buttons. They were purple, blue, green, yellow, and orange. The shiny brass nickel lever to their left had words to the right of it including Normal, Auto, and Warp.

Champo said, "The five colored buttons correspond to the tunnel we enter into and represent what is to be learned there. Before we enter, I will have you depress the corresponding button for that tunnel. The colors also correlate to the original five chakra points on a person's body prior to the seven we commonly refer to today. The button you will now press is the purple one. Remember what I told you at my hut, you must empty your cup."

I went to press the purple button and for the first time noticed the symbol of a small flag in the center. That flag is where I placed the tip of my right index finger and when I pressed it, a surge of purple power rose up through the bottom of my feet and coursed through my nervous system. It felt like a wave of forgiveness was flowing sacredly through me as we shot into the purple tunnel at warp speed.

The LED light from above turned from amber to purple, the chocolate brown panels at the ceiling turned purple, and a fine, sweet, lavender-smelling mist was sprayed into our train car. I looked up at Einstein and he was happily bopping up and down on his bamboo perch. The Sacred Elder's dress remained white and her hair became an even deeper lavender.

Champo continued, "Lavender was initially known as the fragrance and color of forgiveness, as it helped in opening one's crown chakra. While we warp through tunnel one, it will feel and appear as though we are stopping while working with various model projections with our hands moving through the air. The projections on the window screens before us will be of various lessons and teachings on the topic of forgiveness. Remember to empty your cup and be okay not knowing at all times."

The Sacred Elder rose from her seat and joined us at the front of the car. She stood to my left, depressed one of the small square white buttons with an unrecognizable symbol on it and waved her right hand through the air from left to right until the word **FORGIVENESS** appeared at the center of the middle window before us.

Einstein flew off his perch, landed on Champo's right shoulder and said, "Forgiveness, awk, forgiveness."

"That's right Einstein," said the Sacred Elder.

"Let's teach David about forgiveness so he learns it and can then join us in teaching others about the healing qualities it possesses."

For the next several minutes, as we appeared motionless within the purple tunnel, the train flew at warp speed three-inches above the tracks, as the Sacred Elder whizzed both hands across the windows in front of us triggering lessons on the sacred act of forgiveness.

"As we see projected before our eyes, it says 'People forgive for a variety of reasons.' As we learn them, so shall we teach them in order for people to heal. And so it is with each of the five tunnels we pass through today. The buttons I continue to press, with ancient symbols on them, are channeling through my waving hands onto the screens. David, please reach down below the shiny lever, open the wood compartment, and take out the black-and-white speckled composition notebook and the pen."

I removed the composition book and pen. The pen was unique in that it resembled the BIC model that provides four ink colors in one accessible style. This pen was similar, although it had a white stem and five color options to choose from, matching the small square buttons of our dashboard with the simple push of a button. There were the same purple, blue, green, yellow, and orange ink options.

I took the thin plastic clear wrapping off the book, tossed it into the compartment where the book was, opened the book to the first page, and clicked the purple button on the pen. The Sacred Elder whizzed her right hand across the three windows and the phrase, "The Reasons People Forgive," appeared across them.

With the pen ready to glide easily across the page, Einstein hopped down and began to dance rhythmically and intentionally across the symbolized buttons while the Sacred Elder's hands flew through the air.

The pen started moving within the grasp of my right index, middle, and thumb digits without my forcing it. Entering into a mode of no-thought and non-attachment as an observer, I watched the following phrases appear on the first page:

The Reasons People Forgive

Forgiveness sets you free

Forgiveness helps you get unstuck in your life

Forgiveness initiates the healing process

Forgiveness gives you the key to unlock your angered locked heart

Forgiveness returns your power over to you

Forgiveness frees you from the prison you did not realize you were in

Forgiveness helps you let go of resentment and thoughts of revenge

Einstein flew back onto Champo's right shoulder, the Sacred Elder brought her arms down to her sides, and I rested the pen down on the book.

The Sacred Elder said, "David, please read each phrase that appeared on page one."

I read each line, which had the benefits of instilling forgiveness deeper within me.

"Now, let us all think for a moment about those in our lives we have come across where we felt hurt by their words and-or their actions. Was it a parent, co-worker, professor, or partner? Did you experience a trauma where you were physically or emotionally abused by someone close to you? The subsequent wounds have the strong power to leave us with feelings of anger, betrayal, animosity, and even retaliation. Watch on the window screens and you will see what I am referring to."

The Sacred Elder whizzed her hands through the air and scenes flashed quickly in front of us. Parents were heard yelling loudly at their children, co-workers were seen disagreeing loudly across the conference table, a college professor forcefully berating a student in front of the entire class, and supposed lovers raising their voices at each other.

Einstein called out, "No Bueno, awk, no bueno."

Champo said, "That's right Einstein, no bueno."

The Sacred Elder continued, "Now we see the state of current affairs that scar people, leaving them hurt and stuck in their lives. By not practicing forgiveness, these people often pay dearly. The act that hurt or offended them might always be there, but forgiveness can lessen the tight hold it has on those we now see frozen on the screens before us. It may in fact lead to feelings of insight, understanding, and empathy for the one who hurt them. Forgiveness brings a peace that helps them go on in their life."

Einstein hopped back onto the dashboard, clicked several more buttons, and flipped switches as if he were a proficient telephone switchboard operator in New York City in the 1940's. The Sacred Elder flew both hands across the windows, revealing the words, "Effects of Holding Onto Resentment." I wrote that as the heading on page two of my composition book and watched as Einstein and The Sacred Elder pressed buttons and manipulated exacting phrases across the screens. With pen in hand, this is what followed:

Effects of Holding Onto Resentment –

Have no life meaning or purpose

Become unhappy or worried

Become resistant to spiritual and personal growth

Bring anger and hostility into every new
*   relationship*

Sense a lack of enhanced connection with others

Become so bound to the past wrongdoing that you don't enjoy the present

Einstein flew back onto Champo's right shoulder, the Sacred Elder again brought her arms down to her sides, and I rested the pen down on the book.

The Sacred Elder said, "David, please read each phrase that appeared on page two."

I read each line, which had the Effects of Holding Onto Resentment instilled deeper within me.

"Now, let us all think for a moment about those in our lives we have kept in a prison cell and have not forgiven. Think about the billions of people on the planet who are strapped in resentment and do not know any way out of their plight. It's enough to cause the sickness and disease we currently witness around us. We will bring the important message of letting go of resentment to the people and how forgiving oneself and others will bring them out of a victim mentality and into a victor mentality.

I felt complete with the forgiveness exercise but it appeared that a bit more was on the way when Champo said, "Perch" and Einstein flew up above us. Champo joined the Sacred Elder and zigzagged his hands across the windows, cutting and pasting phrases and bits of information that seemed to be the tail end of the messages from the buttons Einstein last pressed.

I took the pen and with the same purple ink, glided my hand across page three, jotting down what appeared to be the remainder of the lessons on Forgiveness. There was no decisive topic or title, merely bits and pieces overflowing through as follows:

Commit to move from suffering to forgiveness

Recognize the value in forgiving

Release the toxic buildup from harmful emotions

Identify who needs to be forgiven and for what

Forgiveness is a personalized process of growth,
expansion, and healthy change

That was that. I clicked the purple tab in the top of the pen and rested it on the book. I closed the pages on the pen and stuck the book under my left armpit. Champo walked back to where he stood before walking over to the dashboard, clicked his tongue twice and Einstein flew back onto his left shoulder.

"Forgiveness heals, awk, forgiveness heals," came from Einstein.

"Yes it does," said the Sacred Elder. "And we also must remember that people will come before us seeking healing who just aren't ready to forgive. In that case, we must remind them to practice empathy and put themselves in the other person's shoes. This does not validate that what the offender did is correct; we are aiming to bring peace to the sufferer. Suggest they begin by writing in a journal and bringing guided meditation into their life. They can also talk with a trusted friend, one of us, or a loved one."

With all of the messages and images now off the screen, it momentarily sat blank. Just when we thought the Forgiveness lesson was over, the train had something else in mind. No buttons were pressed and no arms were waved. The train itself flashed the final forgiveness lesson on the screen which read:

"Self-Forgiveness"

I opened the composition book, clicked the purple ink tab and wrote Self-Forgiveness, and what quickly followed, on page four.

Identify and recognize the wrongs you have done
See how they have affected others

Apologize to the one you have harmed
Express how sorry you are and how you regret
　what you did
Take complete ownership of your wrongdoing
Ask them for forgiveness but do not coerce them
　into it … it may require time
When you can first start forgiving yourself, then
　you will be able to begin forgiving others

The Sacred Elder and Champo looked at each other. Knowing that the lesson and teachings on forgiveness were now complete, she nodded to him and he said, "When we forgive another and ourself, we release a dreadful burden we've carried around for months, years, or even an entire lifetime. This part of our identity is now gone and we are freed from this toxic pain."

I felt a renewed sense of lightness and ease inside myself, the train car, Champo, and the Sacred Elder. Feeling this good from learning about the concepts and principles of forgiveness brought a heightened excitement for what lay before us on these steel wheels. I walked to the smooth mahogany wood file holder at the right front wall of the car and placed the composition book and pen inside.

A high-pitched wailing and feverish beeping poured from the main control board, accompanied by the train emitting a long air decompression hiss as we warped out of Tunnel One and rested back onto the shiny steel tracks. The reconnection contact below provided the same feeling as when the last piece of a puzzle perfectly snapped down into its resting place.

The two translucent rectangular pieces of glass on either side of the car retracted into the mahogany wood trim, allowing fresh air to permeate the cabin. The lavender scent left and the temporary purple accents inside the car returned to their original chocolate brown.

The Sacred Elder went to the control panel, flipped a few white illuminated switches, and the deafening noises shut off. She breathed a sigh of relief, although the look on her face told a somewhat different story.

She explained it to us, "For many generations, these reliable tracks carried multitudes of passengers through the Five Tunnels of Avalon where they'd experience healing and full life expression at the conclusion of the experience. In those ancient times, people were more interested in self-realization and actualization than they are today.

Typically, a second underpass, known as The Tunnel of Love, would have already appeared before us, which we'd enter and travel through similar to the first tunnel. It has not arisen, which means that the train itself has taken over and has something else in store for us entirely."

"I guess we'll have to just be okay not knowing what is next and surrender to the now," said Champo.

From his perch, Einstein yelled out, "Not knowing is knowing, awk, not knowing is knowing."

"Look out the window to our left," said Champo. A white brick building emerged and where the word FORGIVENESS resided at Station One, there was a large black bold ?. We shrugged our shoulders and made the decision to simply be and allow the train to take it from here.

CHAPTER TWELVE

REVERSE SNOW GLOBE

Out of the left window of the train car, we saw Sampson, the Morcubus, flying gently through the air several times, as if trying to send us a message. The Sacred Elder reached into her pouch, removed a pinch of ash, and rubbed it into her third eye.

Closing her other two, she said to us, "Sampson is letting us know that beyond these tracks lies a once great and magnificent park where seekers of ancient truth and mystical knowledge traveled from near and far to walk its sacred grounds and ride its magically transformative attractions. We remain aboard and are soon to experience something elaborate and awe-inspiring."

The Sacred Elder opened her eyes, poured a small mound of ash into her left palm, turned toward the front windows and purposefully blew it at them. Out before us, the open landscape wondrously turned into

a winter wonderland. An entirely snowcapped mountain arrived and along with it, a naturally carved tunnel
within the bedrock, which surrounded us and the entire
expanse of track ahead.

Sampson flew off in the direction of the waterfalls and
the snow flurries picked up their pace and volume, turning
into a full-on white-out blizzard. Steam started to surge out
of the train's smokestack above, while our car simultaneously began heating up quickly below our chilled feet.

Champo said, "This is all completely brand new. I
have ridden this train thousands of times, taking the
masses through the tunnels and back. Not once has this
occurred. It's as if the train is inviting us to create what
happens next versus it doing it for us. David, how do
you recommend we proceed?"

I thought for a moment and replied, "From what I
have learned so far on this journey today, people are rid-
dled with much fear, worry, and anxiety. Spending the
majority of time in either the past or the future, they
miss out on their life while it is occurring in the present
moment. I suggest we grab hold of the shiny brass nickel
lever, throw it into Warp and see how far those tracks
beneath will carry us."

Champo and the Sacred Elder looked at one another, nodded, and Champo said, "Works for us!"

Einstein chimed in and uttered, "Works for me, awk, works for me too."

I continued, "There we have it. We're all in favor of full steam ahead, being okay not-knowing, and accepting this present moment for the invitation it is providing us right here and right now."

The steam above us diminished considerably, which was ideal because the inside of the car was already nice and toasty. My cheeks had warmed and I could sense they took on a rosy glow, matching the warm and fuzzy feeling I had inside. The excitement for the three of us became palpable and we walked together to the illuminated dashboard controls immediately before us.

The white flashing buttons on the dashboard now contained one definitive snowflake at its center. The purple, blue, green, yellow, and orange buttons corresponding to the now non-existent Tunnels of Avalon, became white, and the center of each contained the symbol of a small black flag.

The Sacred Elder said, "David, will you do us the honor of taking us to the next phase of growth and transformation?"

"It would be my sincere pleasure," I exclaimed.

I went over to the shiny lever and grasped the warmed metal. Einstein flew down to Champo's right shoulder, and I lifted the lever from its current "Neutral" state a click up into "Warp."

Champo called out, "And in 3, 2, 1" the train rose three-inches off the tracks and the car we stood in morphed itself into a transparent tube, full-on glass, as though we were standing in a snow globe. Instead of a miniature city or town being in the car with us, the scene was visibly outside, all around, and enveloping us.

It was a magical mystery spectacle, where we observed the translucent car hovering above the snowed-in tracks below, while the flakes danced all around us as white blankets.

The Sacred Elder said, "As we can see out ahead, there resides a brand new and unknown naturally formed tunnel covered by the white rounded and sharp ridges of thick rock. This tunnel represents for us the sacred unknown. As we pass through it, we will have the ability to consciously manifest where and how we end up. Okay, David, proceed please."

I took the shiny brass nickel lever from the "Warp"

setting and pushed it up another click into "Warp II." We catapulted into the carved tunnel and the crystal clear train car became infused with a mixture of snow-flakes and the sweet, hot scent of cinnamon spice. It was beginning to look and smell a lot like Christmas, all throughout the car.

I imagined holding the solid handle of a white ce-ramic mug with a green, red, and white candy cane painted on, while slowly sipping piping hot chocolate, la-dened with tiny white marshmallows. I quickly brought my focus and attention back to the control panel, notic-ing the switches and buttons which were once brilliantly flashing solid white, completely dormant.

The train picked up even greater speed and the echoes of, "On the other side of your biggest fears re-sides your greatest freedom," bounced feverishly off the tunnel walls and reverberated through the glass we were encased within.

Einstein yelled, "Fear to freedom, awk, Fear to free-dom."

With the enhanced super-warp speed, the three of us felt like we were in suspended animation and did not know if we were moving, stationary, going forward, or backward. Our glass enclosure began to take on a wavy liquid appearance and then immediately iced over. We heard the crystallization process and witnessed thousands of iced flakes take over the glass.

We started to shiver, as all remaining heat evaporated. Champo hurried to the back of the car, opened a small mahogany closet door, and produced two more Train Conductor blue coats. He handed one to me and the Sacred Elder and we immediately put them on and buttoned up.

A loud piercing siren started to wail and a red light strobed and bounced off the inner glass in all directions. To complicate matters even more, Einstein began mimicking the siren while bouncing up and down on Champo's right shoulder.

With no warning, the siren stopped, the red flashing ended, and our glass tube immediately reverted back into the ancient Pullman brown train with its familiar Cuban Mahogany wood accents and chocolate brown paneling above. The train came out of Warp II speed and in super slow motion, we elevated higher off the tracks and flew through the tunnel at a snail's pace.

We stood shoulder to shoulder, walked backwards

and sat thigh to thigh to thigh on the plaid cushion seats. I was at the left, the Sacred Elder in the middle, and Champo on the right. We looked ahead out the center window and observed a solid white-brick wall on which we were on a collision course.

CHAPTER THIRTEEN
AMUSEMENT PARK OF TRANSFORMATION

The turtle's pace at which the train drifted through the air, provided the opportunity for each of us to clearly visualize the large black capitalized lettering at the end of our line. The letters read, "The Amusement Park At Avalon Lake."

We each grabbed hold of the wood handles at our sides, Champo called out, "Perch," Einstein flew ten feet above, wrapped his zygodactyl feet around thick green bamboo, and we all closed our eyes.

"Remember to practice your ancient breathing technique right now," reminded the Sacred Elder, as the ancient and beautiful brown beast brought itself out of slow motion and abruptly warped itself through the white brick wall. Pieces of hardened white clay with black embossed lettering flew at great speed in every direction and were heard crumbling to the ground.

When the fifth car was fully through the blasted wall, the train settled, hovering parallel to the ground, let out an air decompression hiss and its steel wheels dropped comfortably back down onto the shiny steel railroad tracks. The side windows opened and the scent of freshly popped pop-corn, hot dogs, and cotton candy infiltrated the car.

We let go of our tight grips on the Cuban mahogany wood handles, stood up, and collectively waited for instructions as a team.

The train blasted three thunderous whistles, introducing a secret compartment door to our right. The door depressurized, unlocked, and opened. Champo called, "Down," and Einstein glided easily onto his right shoulder. They exited the car first and were followed by the Sacred Elder. I took my backpack off the front row seat, grabbed the black and white speckled composition book with the colored pen from the wood pocket on the brown wall, and excitedly exited behind them.

A rising plume of grey smoke surrounded us and the front car of the train we had just departed. We turned around to view it and as the fumes dissipated, marveled at the giant brown beauty, which miraculously did not have one single scratch or dent on her.

The three of us brought our hands to our chest palms together and bowed several times at the Pullman Brown, thanking it for such an amazing journey. Three separate and distinct trumpets of steam protruded through the smokestack of the front car, acknowledging our sincere thanks and bidding us adieu.

All of the fine grey exhaust cleared; turning around from the train we came face-to-face with a beautiful black wrought-iron arched sign that read in rich gold lettering, "Welcome to the Amusement Park at Avalon Lake." The archway entrance stood forty-feet above and was at least one hundred feet wide. Ten turnstiles prevented us from entering the gates, so we stopped and listened attentively for instructions.

While we waited, I looked beyond the gates and noticed the antiquity of the grounds. There were ancient shuttered roller coasters, water rides, transport rides through water and air, and the more gentle rides for children.

I took a visual impression of all within my sight, closed my eyes, and heard the thrilling screams of couples, families, and children of multiple generations past. In my vision, I saw the dazzling display of an elaborate evening fireworks show, with purple, blue, green, yellow, and orange coils, bursts, and sparkling colorful rain.

There was a final tremendous bang that triggered me to open my eyes. It came from the grassy noll beyond the closed gates, where smoke followed the firing of what appeared to be the Dardanelles Gun, the oldest cannon in the world. The giant bronze turquoise barrel rested snug on a gigantic grey-black carriage with two architecturally brilliant eight-spoked wheels.

The Sacred Elder said, "This park, up until right now, has been legend and myth. Champo and I have heard of its existence through discourse from ancient mystical elders at sacred meetings throughout time. Because we have been led to it, our next phase of learning will ensue aboard its mystical rides and attractions. Instead of warping through four more tunnels aboard the Pullman Brown, we will be guided to and through specific parts of Avalon to learn, experience, and delight.

"The Elders we came across many generations ago, spoke of the time when a group of three truth seekers will meet up with a fourth at these ancient grounds. Their work off the usual tracks would signify a time when a fifth member will soon join them, completing what is referred to esoterically as the *Infinity Star Team.*"

She was finished speaking and three of the ten turnstiles we stood before began clicking and calibrating themselves. A low whirring noise emitted from within each one and their small square digital displays came to life at the top surfaces. We looked at the digital instructions at our separate turnstiles which read, "Insert Red Ticket Below."

At the slot where the tickets get inserted, several more clicking sounds began, and a suction sound followed. I remembered that the Sacred Elder and I put our red tickets through the slot on the train. Champo knew exactly what I was thinking and said, "No need to go back on the train, David," and he reached into the top front right pocket of his navy blue three-piece suit and produced three red tickets. He handed one to me and the Sacred Elder and at the same time, we placed them at the whirring slots.

They disappeared into the shiny brass nickel and we stood back in awe as the glowing silver turnstile bars spun with incredible velocity, vanished, inviting us majestically into the park.

We walked through our individual stall and approached the Dardanelles Gun at the grassy noll. The massive bronze turquoise cannon greeted us on the other side of the entrance gates by shooting another mammoth black ball from its guts. The loud boom echoed across the front of the park, sparking the colorful beds of water lilies, bleeding hearts, birds of paradise, cherry blossoms, orchids, and tulips into a wonderful dance.

When the echoing ceased, the loud chirping of crickets and grasshoppers ensued, while green dragonflies surrounded us, making faint clucking sounds, and summoning us to follow them.

We marched on and after several twists and turns, meandered through the park and passed several shutdown ancient rides, tarp-covered funnel cake, chicken tender, and cotton candy huts, where a wonderful bouquet of green and red hummingbirds greeted us. The dragonflies zigzagged through the flock and hurried off. The hummingbirds were joined by a kaleidoscope of monarch butterflies and the grouping of beautiful creatures led us deeper into the closed park.

CHAPTER FOURTEEN

LOVE

Another large black wrought-iron arched sign, similar to the one greeting us at the park entrance, hovered a few feet in front and high above us. In the same gold lettering it read, "Transformation Land." Pressing on into this themed section, our new colorful bird and butterfly friends escorted us to the entrance of The Tunnel of Love attraction. Einstein called out, "Tunnel of Love awk, Tunnel of Love." We walked through the long maze of silver crowd control poles and arrived inside the pitch-black tunnel.

The Sacred Elder took out her small lavender crystal, drew a tiny pinch of ash from the pouch, and sprinkled it over the stone. A soft purple glow illuminated the darkened catacomb, revealing a river of gently flowing water and several ancient wooden four-passenger boats. The vessels were rocking in the water from side to side creating splashes and knocking noises against the concrete platform to which they were fastened.

The big question that entered my mind and exited my mouth was, "How will the Tunnel of Love start-up after all of the time it's been shut down?"

No one answered. Champo and Einstein stood patiently waiting, while the Sacred Elder looked at me and then back down at her small brown leather pouch. She cupped her left hand, dumped a small mound of burnt Hyperion ash onto it, took a deep breath in, and blew it at the grey dust. The ride magically came to life. The blue boats had horizontal turquoise stripes painted across their sides and were adorned with large white wood-carved swan ornaments at the front tip.

To get into the boat, we grabbed onto the tall metal poles bolted to the concrete, and stepped on one foot at a time. Champo, with Einstein on his right shoulder, and the Sacred Elder sat in the front row and I sat in the second. The bacteria and germs that penetrated the boat after years of no use, created that old wood smell. We felt the old vessel move underneath us and we glided easily toward the dark tunnel. The white swan got absorbed by the darkness and we were enveloped by it next.

The forward motion of the craft brought some comfort but the pitch black mustered-up some uneasiness within me. Champo called out, "Remember to be okay not knowing. If you were in a dimly lit room at home all by yourself and intentionally shut your eyes, you'd be in total darkness by choice. Pretend for a moment that you are choosing this and drop any resistance you may feel."

I closed my eyes, even though I could not see with them open, and repeated the words in my mind, "I am choosing this. I am choosing this."

I followed the affirmation with several deep breaths and on the last forceful exhalation through my mouth, I felt the boat rise off its submerged metal track and raise three-inches out of the water. I opened my eyes, looked at the back of Champo, The Sacred Elder, and Einstein's heads while the boat turned itself ¼ to its left. We continued to float down the river and the left wall I assumed we were now facing began to exhibit a soft white glow. It took on the appearance of a white brick wall and Champo began to speak.

"Look at the white brick wall before us."

Champo raised his right hand, brought his thumb

and middle finger together, and produced a loud "snap!" Einstein flew off his right shoulder to the brick wall, waved his right zygodactyl foot across the wall through the air and the word LOVE appeared on the bricks in bold thick black lettering. Einstein flew onto the large white swan head carving at the head of the boat and nestled there while Champo continued.

"As we bring our attention to the word LOVE inscribed on the white brick, breathe deeply into your heart chakra the symbolic essence of love's representation, which is a life experience of internal happiness."

The boat continued to glide gently to our right and the E from the word LOVE left our peripheral vision. The white brick wall slowly moved to our left and the Sacred Elder said, "There is no such thing as something being like something else. As Champo told us on the train before we entered the tunnel of Forgiveness, we must now empty our cups again in order to experience the fullness and richness of the Tunnel of Love."

I emptied my mind of all I experienced prior to this moment and surrendered any anticipation. I grounded myself and was completely still within. Champo took off his military style pillbox hat with his left hand, placed it on the seat between him and the Sacred Elder, ran the fingers of his right hand through his thick black hair, and spoke again.

"This ancient tunnel we currently find ourselves in represents the original Tunnel of Love and is the second attraction of five total sacred experiences we will have at Avalon. The first was the purple Tunnel of Forgiveness combined with the Winter Wonderland. Again, keep in mind, it is of the utmost importance that you remain okay not knowing."

The Sacred Elder poured another small grey mound of ash onto her cupped left palm and brought a new small clear crystal out from her leather pouch. She held it at the edge of her left fingertips and before blowing on it, said, "We do not love to be loved. We simply love for the sake of doing so."

She breathed deeply and energetically blew the dust at the clear crystal. A surge of powerful clear-blue ocean waves rose up through the bottom of the wood boat and into my feet. Coursing through my nervous system, I sensed the mighty flooding of love flowing naturally through me as we easily glided to our right deeper within the Love tunnel.

The light turned from whitish amber to soft turquoise while a fine sweet ocean mist sprayed freely throughout. I looked at the helm of the craft and observed Einstein as his feathers became mostly white with turquoise highlights. He happily danced in circles on the perch of the white swan head. The Sacred Elder's dress remained white and the purple streaks in her hair turned to turquoise.

Champo continued, "Turquoise was originally known as the fragrance and color of love before the popularized red came into play. Turquoise aids in the opening of the third-eye chakra, giving access and incredible insight into what true love is about. This we will be learning in great depth and detail shortly.

"As we continue to glide above the water and to our right it will at times feel and appear as though we are stopped. Do not allow your mind to trick you while we are pressing on. Since this is our first experience at the Amusement Park let's sit in still silence as the tunnel teaches us about the sacredness of Love, our second of Five FLAGS."

The Sacred Elder extended her right arm and pointed the clear crystal at Einstein. He rose from the swan head, flew over to the blue bricked wall and pur-posefully waved his feet at it like the conductor of a moving symphony.

I instinctively produced the black and white com-position book from my backpack and unclipped the multi-colored pen from the front cover. I depressed the turquoise blue tab and opened the book to the blank page 5. The word LOVE appeared once again on the bricks and I wrote it at the top of the blank page in tur-quoise ink.

Einstein flew back onto the swan-head perch, and screamed, "Love heals, awk, love heals."

"That's right, Einstein. Love certainly does heal. Let's sit back together and learn the qualities of love so we may in turn teach others about the healing qualities it possesses," said the Sacred Elder.

She then produced a turquoise crystal from her pouch and whizzed both crystals through the air before us. A solid, dark image of a man appeared against the brighter brick background. I held the pen, ready to glide turquoise ink easily across the page; Einstein again hopped up and down and began to dance rhythmically in circles over the swan's bald white head. The combination of bird-feet twirling and crystals zigzagging prompted the dark image on the blue hued bricks to speak about love.

His poetic words illuminated in large black lettering to the left and right of the word LOVE, as the vessel we sat in, appeared to be motionless.

The pen started moving within the grasp of my right index, middle, and thumb digits without my pushing it. With the surge of ocean wave energy promulgating up through me, I once again entered into a mode of no-thought and non-attachment as a simple silent watcher. I gratefully listened to the man and watched as the following phrases appeared on the wall and then on page five:

The Benefits of Love –

Love makes you happy

Love reduces stress

Love lessens anxiety

Love has you focus more on self-care

Love contributes to longevity

Love boosts the immune system

The image stopped speaking and Einstein stopped twirling. The Sacred Elder brought the clear and blue stones down to her sides, and I rested the pen on the opened book.

The Sacred Elder said, "David, please read each phrase that appeared on the wall."

I read each line, which had the benefits of love instilled deeper within me.

She continued, "Now, let us all think for a moment about those in our lives we love. Who do you see in your mind? Is it a parent, grandparent, sibling, child, pet, or partner? What loving experiences have you had with them? How did those experiences make you feel? Really get in touch with how love makes you feel. That's good. Feel it in every cell and fiber of your being. Let's watch together and you will see what I am referring to."

The Sacred Elder shot white and blue energy from the crystals at the wall and scenes flashed quickly in front of us.

It was as if we were standing still on a conveyer belt moving slowly to our right through the Tunnel of Love, watching the scrolling scenes move effortlessly across the wall. Parents were lifting their children high in the air and we heard them laughing uncontrollably. Grandparents were sitting with their grandchildren on soft cotton blankets in the park, bouncing them on their knees, while reading stories to them. We heard the sweet sounds of blue jays calling across tall crabapple fruit trees to their mates.

A brother was emotionally delivering a beautiful heartfelt speech at his sister's wedding on the pure white sands of Florida's Emerald Coast. A little girl handed her mother a beautiful bouquet of Himalayan Blue Poppy's at the conclusion of her mother's solo violin concerto at a Tibetan Buddhist temple. A dog licked the face of its owner who had just arrived home from a long business trip overseas. Lovers held hands on a blue park bench, gazing deeply into each other's eyes and seeing the moon's reflection in them.

Einstein again called out, "Love heals, awk, love heals."

The Sacred Elder waved the crystals through the air, the solid silhouette image appeared, and spoke to us.

"Now you see the power of love before your eyes. Experiencing love has countless health and life benefits. When people let love find them and all guards are down, they embrace it with open arms. Too many people, because of a lack of affection in childhood, cross their arms over their chest and are therefore left holding only themselves. You must be willing to take the risk, uncross your arms and be okay embracing another or being embraced yourself. Be the lover and okay not being loved in return."

The image stopped speaking and the Sacred Elder brought the crystals down.

We continued to glide to our right, the solid silhouette image dissolved, and the blue brick walls were blank slates once more. Champo brought his body into a lotus meditation posture on the wood bench and began his wonderful discourse.

"Now, I will share with you, "Effects of Lack of Love."

I wrote that as the heading on page six of my composition book and both the Sacred Elder and I listened as Champo continued.

"Love deprivation often results in ...

Unhappiness

Loneliness

Depression

Stress

Poor health

Mood Swings

Anxiety

Immune System Suppression

"David, please read each phrase that you wrote down on page six."

I read each line, which had the Effects of Lack of Love instilled deeper within me, and Champo continued.

"Now, let us all think for a moment about those in our lives and those who are not, who do not have love in their life. Think about the millions of people on the planet who are trapped in loveless relationships and do not know of any way out of their predicament. So much sickness and disease is the result of these unfortunate and oftentimes unnecessary situations. We will bring the important message of consciously manifesting love to the people and how a life of love is one worth living."

Champo finished his wonderful discourse and I

kept my pen in hand, feeling another wave of Love information about to come through. But not just yet. The tunnel had other ideas. It again went completely black. Champo shouted, "Remain," Einstein stayed cemented on the white swan head, and the vessel turned itself ¼ back to its original forward position. I waited for the Sacred Elder to blow some grey fairy dust through another crystal to illuminate us but nothing came.

In the distance, several evenly spaced out sky blue light bulbs brought their soft light into the tunnel from above, and all we had to do was wait patiently until we caught up with them.

"The perfect opportunity for each of us to practice our ancient breathing technique," said the Sacred Elder.

The first blue bulb arrived above us and the boat stopped in the air. It then let out an air decompression sound and slowly settled back down onto the ancient and cool waters below. It reconnected itself with the steel track, and we continued forward as more soft blue glow lamps passed over us above.

There was no more crystal magic projecting onto the walls or ceiling. Einstein flew back onto the right shoulder of Champo, and the composition book remained open on my lap, with the pen awaiting its next move.

The blue bulbs above flashed as if we were dancing at Studio 54 on a Saturday evening in 1977. The waters beneath us took on a blue and white lava-lamp form, and the tunneled attraction took over completely. It began to speak in a deep, suave, meditative Barry White voice. I took the pen and with the same blue ink, glided my hand across page seven, jotting down the following lessons on self-love, while listening to Barry's groovy and soulful voice.

> *Self-love involves setting healthy boundaries*
>
> *Self-love means putting high value on your own happiness*
>
> *Self-love means not giving up your well-being for others' needs and wants*
>
> *Self-love is having a positive view of yourself*
>
> *Self-love means you are confident in your place in the world*
>
> *Self-love is knowing when to say "No"*

These simple ways to practice Self-love speak volumes and will help those needing to fill their love-tank a bit more:

Speak kind words to yourself

Have a sense of gratitude for what you already *possess in life*

Repeat positive and loving affirmations throughout the day

Bring yourself to the present moment

And remember that no matter what you have or have not done, you are worthy of love

The expressive voice went into a blissful low humming, and coupled with the blue and white lava flowing beneath us the tone and mood set even deeper into love's vault. The boat followed the track beneath it to the right and I felt the ride was coming to a close.

In the distance, I observed a white brick wall with large black letters that read, "Love Never Ends," written in an arched formation. Under the sign were two large black doors. As we made our way slowly toward the doors, the voice spoke once more.

"Before you all leave, let's make this ride complete by

sharing with you the ancient ways to demonstrate love."

On page eight in my notebook I wrote, "Ways to Demonstrate Love," at the top. The rest of what I wrote on that subject, which came eloquently from the voice above, is as follows:

Random Acts of Kindness

Lending a helping hand

Gift Giving

Quality Time

Physical Touch

Encouraging Words

Listen for the Gold in what the other is saying

Practice Forgiveness

When you can first start loving yourself, then you will be able to truly love others.

The black doors opened outward just before the white head of the swan pendant entered and we entered daylight at the end of The Tunnel of Love Attraction.

The voice bid us farewell: "Enjoy the rest of your time at the Amusement Park at Avalon Lake."

The front of our boat gently bumped the unoccupied blue one in front of it and when we stopped, Champo got off with Einstein, followed by the Sacred Elder, and then me.

"What a ride!" said Champo. "Now we have some useful information to bring to the people on the topic of Love, the second Flag."

"It was amazing," said the Sacred Elder. "The myths and folklore of the stories we were told about this place were spot-on. Look, here are our friendly hummingbird and butterfly escorts. Let's greet them and see where they are going to lead us next," she added.

"David, what did you learn from the Tunnel of Love?" asked Champo.

"I learned that when we love another as ourself, we see them as the pure conscious essence they are. Instead of seeing them solely as a limited personality, we are able to engage them at the stillness level that matters most. It is from this sacred space where true love and relatedness arise."

I took the notebook and pen and placed them into my backpack. Champo, Einstein, and the Sacred Elder followed the butterflies and birds and I was right behind them. The sun above us was blazing off the concrete, warming us from above and from below up through us. Still, most of the attractions were shuttered, yet knowing a few customers were meandering through, one popcorn vendor opened his colorful red, yellow, and white stand.

"Three please," I said to him.

"That'll be ten dollars even, sonny."

I reached into a side pocket of my backpack, produced a $10 bill, and handed it to the man dressed in a white shirt, beige khaki's, and an apron made out of red, yellow, and white fabric. He appeared to have eaten his fair share of amusement park delights over the years. When he handed me the three overflowing medium-sized paper bags of popcorn, several pieces fell to the ground during the exchange. Einstein swooped in for a quick snack.

I thanked the vendor, handed Champo and the Sacred Elder their popcorn bags, and we ate while following our escorts through the remaining attractions within Transformation Land.

CHAPTER FIFTEEN

ACCEPTANCE

The hummingbirds and butterflies huddled together in deep conversation between two rides. It was beautiful to observe them hovering in suspended animation before a beautiful backdrop of dark, fragrant, towering pine trees. They appeared to have come to a collective and unanimous decision and led us to the entrance of our next attraction.

We stood before a quite large and completely enclosed cylindrical dome. It had dark green walls, a beige roof, and white steel framed letters with white illuminated bulbs within them spelling the word ROTOR. At the top third of the ride, there appeared to be an observation deck for non-riders to watch from. We took the ramp pathway on our right and walked up the concrete incline while being completely dwarfed by the green massive dome on our left.

"Is this what I think it is?" asked the Sacred Elder.

"Perhaps we ought to wait a few minutes before entering, having just consumed the entire contents of popcorn bags," said Champo.

"Ah, let's live like we were small children. We would have consumed a slice of pizza, a hot dog, corn on the cob, and with stained shirts immediately hopped on the roller coaster. Let's see what this puppy has to offer," I said.

"He's got a point, awk, he's got a point," said Einstein.

The three of us laughed and entered the dark large upright barrel. The abrasive musty smell coming from the ancient green carpeted floor and walls confronted us. It reminded me of walking into the unfinished basement of my grandparents' home in Queens to fetch folding chairs for the company coming over to Sunday night brisket dinner. I wished the ride smelled as good as my grandma's home cooking.

I placed my backpack down at the entrance floor and removed the composition book and pen. I depressed the dark green tab and wrapped the plastic clip over the front cardboard cover.

We walked into the centrifuge and stood side by side while leaning against the green carpet wall. The only light coming into the dome was from the outside, peeking through the small cracks of the aged beige glass up above.

Champo said, "Perch," and Einstein flew ten feet above onto a shiny metal rail overlooking us at the observation platform. He bounced up and down in excitement, as though he knew exactly what was in store for us.

Champo continued, "Many generations ago, as the stories go, this park was filled with people who had a sincere aim with their personal growth and spiritual expansion. The rides, shows, and attractions provided them with a direct experience of presence, stillness, and conscious awareness. Who the person was before they entered the park was completely different from those who exited. They were deeply affected on these grounds at the spiritual level within themselves that matter most."

Just when he finished speaking, the natural golden light from the sun protruded from above at the appropriate angle, revealing the word ACCEPTANCE in large white letters in the center of the round pine green floor.

Again, there was no activity or motion, as this ride, like The Tunnel of Love prior, has been closed for centuries.

The Sacred Elder reached into the leather pouch tied at the rope belt around her waist and removed an elongated one-inch green stone. "In ancient times, this crystal was known to bring a sense of peace, calm, and acceptance to the holder. Green amethyst was known as a mystical bridge, connecting the solar plexus chakra (seat of acceptance), heart chakra, third eye, and crown chakras. This attraction, once it initiates, will propel us into a mystical whirlwind where the present moment resides."

She poured from the magical pouch, and produced a fine grey mound of dust onto her left palm. Holding the stone at the fingertips of her left hand, the Sacred Elder forcefully inhaled and blew the air out purposefully at the ash. Green sparkles illuminated throughout the rotunda and the ride came to life. Einstein excitedly bounced up and down through the green sparks, while the ride slowly spun on its axis below.

Champo reminded us, "Let's all remember to keep our popcorn where it belongs inside of us and continue to empty our cups in order to experience the breadth and wonder of this ancient ride. The third attraction of

Avalon we're experiencing today is perhaps the most important of the Five FLAGS, in that it represents Acceptance. Stay standing nice and tall and keep your arms and hands pressed tightly against your sides."

We continued to spin and with each revolution, a large white flag fully solidified on the floor underneath the word Acceptance. It became increasing more difficult to move my body, as the G-Forces acted strongly upon it. I thought about how tightly wound up I have been my entire life and how this feeling of not being in control began playing games in my mind. That was when it seemed the Sacred Elder began to read it and spoke to us.

"Acceptance allows for the removal of resistance to the present moment, which leads to a greater appreciation and awareness of life."

Immediately following those words, a surge of powerful roots of a pine tree soared up through the bottoms of our feet and coursed powerfully through veins, arteries, and nerves. I felt a flooding of grounded acceptance flow naturally through me as we spun in the green cylinder at 3G-Force.

The green sparkles evaporated and the entire dome glowed in a lime-green hue. A fine misting of pine, juniper, sandalwood, and citrus sprayed freely into the space around us. When we rotated and caught a dizzying glimpse of Einstein up above, his white feathers appeared accented with green. He was laughing hysterically at us from his metal perch above.

Out of the corner of my right eye, the Sacred Elder's dress remained white and her hair took on newer thin green streaks, having replaced the turquoise. In an instant, everything slowed down considerably, even though we continued to spin at 3G-Force.

This was it, the sacred present moment. It had been here all along, yet my mind was too active with constant thoughts to see it. It was magical and still. The floor we stood upon disappeared beneath us and we slowly slid down the musty green carpet against our backs into the magical pit of Acceptance below. In slow motion, Champo sent out a long whistle, and the green and white Scarlet Macaw flew down to meet us as the floor became our new ceiling.

"Wow, that was something," said Champo.

"You're not kidding. I did everything in my power to keep the popcorn down," said the Sacred Elder.

"We all appreciate that," I laughed.

The pit we found ourselves in was lit up in the same lime coloring as above. There were several empty green cars and we boarded the first one in the same seating configuration as the "Tunnel of Love Boat."

I breathed a huge sigh of relief that I had taken the composition book and pen out of my backpack before getting onto the ROTOR.

The same scent of pine, juniper, sandalwood, and citrus engulfed the underground tube and we slowly moved through a network of twisting and turning concrete tunnels.

As we entered deeper into the tunnel, a warm and sweet female voice spoke to us from multiple black speakers above. "Welcome to the Avenues of Acceptance, a magical underworld journey through the byways of yesteryear, at a time when the Ego was non-existent and resistance to what is was unknown. This slow-moving tram ride, propelled magnetically from beneath you, will glide in and out of multiple attractions, most notably Mystical Mountain, where you will hear and have the opportunity to read about the healing properties and practices of Acceptance. Enjoy your voyage, friends."

The Sacred Elder produced the clear stone from her pouch and pointed it directly in front of us. A bright white glow illuminated the zigzagging tunnels, allowing Champo to read the first huge white sign with green lettering on our left.

"Dating back over one-hundred and forty million years, pine color and fragrance was known for helping with the initiation of acceptance by opening and healing the throat chakra at the midpoint of your neck. With the opening of the throat chakra, access and insight is discovered into what true acceptance is about. This we will be learning in great depth and detail shortly as we continue on. Remember, we all must accept this present moment as it is and continue to be okay not knowing."

The Sacred Elder said, "It seems we'll all have an opportunity to read off signs within these narrow cement green tunnels. David, you'll also read and have the ability to write the information in the notebook at the same time. That is, if this speed remains the same."

The next sign simply had the word ACCEPTANCE written in green against the white backdrop and beneath it there was the symbol of a flag in green. I opened the composition book to Page 9 and wrote Acceptance at the top in green ink. A wave of excitement came over me and I took a nice deep breath in through my nose and exhaled it out of my mouth, sinking deeper into the present moment.

Einstein, who was perched at the front of the car atop a slightly raised eight-inch metal bar, yelled out, "Acceptance now, awk, Acceptance now."

"That's right Einstein. Acceptance brings us to what is in the here and now. Let's journey on and learn together about the qualities of acceptance so we can teach others about the healing qualities it possesses," said Champo.

For the next several minutes we slowly moved on within the green passageways. This was my favorite aroma so far, as it reminded me of the countless nature hikes I took as a young teenager at summer camp through the pine tree forests of upstate New York.

With the surge of pine tree root energy still protruding up through me, I entered into a mode of no-thought and no-doing, simply becoming a silent observer and keen listener. I gratefully sat in stillness and watched as my friends sat in delight in front of me while the following phrases appeared on the white signs passing us slowly to our left and right.

The Benefits of Acceptance

Acceptance heals trauma

Acceptance brings enjoyment and enthusiasm

Acceptance reduces stress, anxiety, and anger

Acceptance brings heightened awareness, centeredness, and focus

Acceptance allows for greater listening and learning

Acceptance creates more stillness and awareness

Acceptance is a gateway into the present moment

I wrote each passing phrase onto Page 9 and then put the pen down on the opened book.

The Sacred Elder said, "David, please read each phrase that appeared on Page 9."

I read each line, which had the benefit of instilling acceptance deeper within all of us.

From the multiple dispersed black speakers above, the same warm and sweet female voice spoke to us once more, "Now, let us all think for a moment about the ancient practice of acceptance. Now that you have observed multiple phrases on the walls, what do you sense the practice of acceptance can do for you and others? Let's watch together through the clear windows on your right and left, as you pass through the bedrock of Mystical Mountain, the power that acceptance produces."

Our green car slowed considerably and the air surrounding us became hotter. We approached the first window on our left and inside the small room was a life-like woman made of fiberglass and plastic. She was dressed for Northeast late October weather, lying face up on a bed of brown, red, and yellow fall leaves, with her arms outstretched above her head. She wore a pleasant grin on her face.

The window left our view and we approached another one on our right. This small room showed a male office worker dressed in grey slacks, a white buttoned-down shirt, and pine green tie, sitting at an old grey metal office desk with stacks of papers and files piled up at various random heights. He wore black-rimmed plastic glasses and on the wall behind him read a sign, "It Is What It Is."

We slowly passed that room and came upon the

final window on our left. This room was double the size of the previous two and it had 10 meditation practitioners sitting in two semi-circle rows, one row behind the other, listening to the instructor providing lessons on the benefits of acceptance. There were several black-framed white posters hanging at various spots on the walls with affirmations on acceptance. I turned to Page 10 in the composition book and wrote every one of them down.

Self-acceptance Daily Affirmations

I am worthy of life

I am worthy of love

I accept myself, flaws and all

I am a beautiful reflection of the entire universe

I am an unfinished product

I choose to accept myself as I am

I am okay not knowing

I release resistance and choose this present
moment as is

I accept both my successes and failures as
learning experiences

We left the rooms behind us, picked up speed again, and thankfully cooled down considerably. I wiped the remaining sweat beads from my forehead with the back of my right hand and watched as Einstein jumped up and down on the small metal bar and called out, "Acceptance now, awk, Acceptance now."

The Sacred Elder said, "Now we see from viewing the three rooms within Mystical Mountain, some examples of how acceptance brings increased happiness, joy, and positive power to one's life. True acceptance means recognizing all facets of our life, even the negative ones, and facing how we feel about them. When we stop and notice the situation we're faced with right now in life and choose willingly what we are required to do, all resistance washes away and we act from the present moment."

We pressed on through the green-lit narrow tunnels and with the increasingly cooler air and natural light coming toward us, I sensed the ride was coming to an end. The track we rode on began to journey up a slight incline to the right, and for the final time we heard the voice coming out of the black speakers above.

"Let us think for a moment about the billions of suffering people on the planet who do not accept and are therefore experiencing so much pain. It's enough to cause the multitude of physical and emotional sicknesses and diseases we currently witness. Contemplate all the amazing effects practicing acceptance creates. You will bring the important messages of letting go and dropping resistance to the people in order to have them go from a life of defiance toward a life of harmony. Journey well, my friends."

Our little green car traveled further into the natural light and just before we entered the full light of day, the car stopped on the track. It made a ¼ turn to its right, pivoting us to face the end of the tunnel. The wall opened to the right and revealed a large mud-brick room with a man kneeling on a Persian rug. The room exhibited an exceptional level of thirteenth-century architectural craftsmanship including barrel vaults, stone relief carvings, and walls decorated with fresco paintings and mosaics.

The older man at the carpet kneeled before us with his chin flexing down to his chest. He wore a thick white beard and a tall knitted gold, red, and black wool head covering. A white shawl wrapped around the hat several times and a brown and blue checkered article of cloth with beige fur at its edges draped over his shoulders.

He extended his hands towards us and gestured with them as he spoke, "I once wrote a poem called *The Guest House*. It was inspired by my friend and teacher, Shams of Tabriz, who opened me up to many wonderful teachings including acceptance, the main theme of the poem. Please enjoy it, my friends."

Rumi recited the poem for us with poise, grandeur, beauty, eloquence, and grace.

"This being human is a guest house.
Every morning a new arrival.

A joy, a depression, a meanness,
some momentary awareness comes
as an unexpected visitor.

Welcome and entertain them all!
Even if they're a crowd of sorrows,
who violently sweep your house
empty of its furniture,
still, treat each guest honorably.
He may be clearing you out
for some new delight.

The dark thought, the shame, the malice,
meet them at the door laughing,
and invite them in.

Be grateful for whoever comes,
because each has been sent
as a guide from beyond.

I hope you enjoyed that poem. Also remember, who could be so lucky. Who comes to a lake for water and sees the reflection of moon. So long, friends. Go forth and teach others how to transform their lives."

The wall slid to left and closed Rumi and the room off from our view. Our tiny green car turned ¼ to the left and came fully out into the natural light of day. The pine trees danced in the gentle breeze while the sun's rays beamed energetically onto us, warming our cells.

The car came to a dead end at the back of the ROTOR attraction and we exited the car onto the concrete platform. I walked briskly down the ramp on the left side of the ride and grabbed my backpack waiting for me at the entrance where I had left it. I put the composition book and pen inside and zipped the pack closed.

The Sacred Elder and Champo caught up with me. The three of us made it to the front of the attraction; looking at the word ROTOR at the dome's façade she said, "What a grand and wonderful opportunity it is simply to be alive and together at this ancient Wonderland. We must always remember to practice acceptance first and then take purposeful action. We choose the actions we want to take out of conscious awareness, while dropping any resistance in the now. We will teach this to the people."

CHAPTER SIXTEEN
GRATITUDE

We pressed on through the beautiful manicured grounds, beds of charming and wonderfully smelling flowers, and exited Transformation Land. Our butterfly and hummingbird escorts flew away from their meals and happily greeted us at the massive black wrought-iron arched sign that read Present World in large white capitalized letters.

Passing by shuttered Tea Cup, Log Flume, and Bumper Car attractions, our winged friends brought us to the entrance of Gratitude Geyser, An Underwater Submarine Quest. The three of us looked at each other with some reservations about being submerged and enclosed in a vessel that has not operated for hundreds of years. Champo reached into his right pocket and fed Einstein a couple leftover pieces of popcorn.

Einstein loved and appreciated the snack, "Delicious and nutritious, awk, Delicious and nutritious."

We laughed at his jovial and free-flowing nature, obviously grateful for the snack, which we used as a sign to drop our reservations about the ride before us.

"We have to be okay not knowing and have gratitude for what we currently have in our lives, which is each other and our health," I said.

The three-foot by six-foot Gratitude Geyser sign for the ride was fastened at the top of a seven-foot yellow pole. The letters were in black on a white backdrop; the border trim of the sign was yellow. We approached the first of four yellow submergible craft, stepped onto the black non-slip strip on its ledge, and one at a time climbed down into the vessel. Einstein joined us, entering the hole in a precise flight pattern.

The scent of sulfurous decay was unpleasant yet tolerable. It was a small enclosed space and I was not ready for the latch to close and seal shut. I had to remind myself of the previous rides' messages regarding acceptance in order to be okay not knowing what was going to occur on this ride. I took a deep breath and dropped the resistance I was feeling in my chest. I looked around the old craft and took a visual impression of the white hard plastic innards and total of twelve windows, six on each side.

The Sacred Elder reached into her leather pouch and revealed a small irregularly shaped yellow stone. She placed it into the palm of her right hand and rested her hand on her right knee. She took the pouch, sprinkled fine whitish-grey dust onto the yellow crystal, placed the pouch in her lap, and spoke to us.

"This Gratitude excursion we are about to have together is necessary in order to attract to our lives those people, places, and things that we want. When we have gratitude for the Now and everything currently existing in our lives, the universe will open doors for us where there was once walls. It will deliver to us what we wish. Think for a moment what an amazingly abundant universe we reside in and how the keys to attraction are found by impressing on it what we desire."

Champo added, "Let's all remember to keep our cups empty in order to fully experience the scope and components of Gratitude. It appears we are in store for a magical underwater experience."

The Sacred Elder raised her right hand off her knee and blew a steady stream of air onto her palm. The inner hull of our mini-ship glowed yellow while thousands of yellow sparkles illuminated. The pink pastel hatch closed and a loud suction noise indicated the hatch was sealed tightly.

The ramp outside raised automatically and we slowly pushed away from the dock. Out of the speakers embedded on the left and right hardened white plastic walls, a pre-recorded male pirate-accented voice spoke, "This is your captain speaking, welcome aboard Gratitude Geyser. All ahead one-third."

The tiny yellow sub propelled a bit faster through the ancient murky waters and the voice continued, "Gratitude has been shown to help individuals in countless ways, including better physical and psychological health, increased happiness and life satisfaction, decreased depression, and more, which you will soon observe."

The Sacred Elder, now that we were moving along at a nice clip, blew on her open right palm once more, propelling the remaining grey Hyperion ash throughout the vessel. A surge of powerful lemon scent infused the entire car. I felt an overflow of aliveness, clarity, and gratitude stream through me as the cloudy waters outside cleared and took on a lemonade glow.

A beige periscope released from the ceiling. Champo stood up and went over to look through it. He grabbed the black rubber handles on either side and called out what he saw above the water.

"David take out your composition book, multi-colored pen, and get ready to write down information on Gratitude. First, turn to the next blank page, depress the yellow tab on the pen, and write the word Gratitude at the top of the page. Directly underneath, draw a picture of a small flag. Gratitude represents the fourth of The Five FLAGS we are experiencing, learning about, and ultimately bringing out to the people."

I finished sketching the yellow flag underneath the word Gratitude and watched as a yellow flag appeared within the frame of the first window on the left side of the sub. I then looked over at Einstein sitting on Champo's right shoulder and noticed his white feathers were now accented with yellow. He happily jumped off, flew around the tiny vessel, and took a perch at the top of the periscope. The Sacred Elder's dress remained white and her hair was now a combination of white with yellow highlights.

Champo backed away from the periscope and the captain's voice came again over the speakers.

"Look out the right windows and observe the descriptive placards. The true origin of lemons is not entirely known, although our sources tell us they may have originated in north-western India. Lemon color and fragrance was originally known for helping with the introduction of gratitude by opening and healing the heart chakra located in the center of your chest at the tiny bumps on the sternum. With the opening of the heart chakra, greater access and understanding into gratitude and attraction are found."

The Sacred Elder rose from her seat and joined Champo at the periscope. She pressed a tiny black button above the left rubber handle and the word GRATITUDE appeared at window next to the one with the flag on it.

Einstein flew off his perch, landed back on Champo's right shoulder and yelled, "Gratitude attracts, awk, Gratitude attracts."

"That's right Einstein. Gratitude brings to us what our hearts desire. Let us all learn together as the lessons of gratitude are instilled deeper in us. Then we will bring these teachings to others so they may experience their amazing transformational qualities," said Champo.

Champo pressed a small yellow button on the left end of the black rubber periscope handle, which had it retract back up flat against the ceiling.

The Sacred Elder and Champo took their seats beside me and the captain's voice spoke to us once more.

"As we dive deeper below the surface, you will begin to view undersea life of an ancient era. This magical lagoon will begin to deliver sacred teachings on the topic of Gratitude. Looking out the window to your right, you will see dense curtains of small yellow bubbles rushing toward the vessel. Watch now, as the seaweed, coral reefs, golden rock formations, and mystical caves bring this ride to life."

Passing through a tall collection of yellow seaweed, we were greeted by a mammoth albino leatherback sea turtle with large yellow patches dispersed over its body. Measuring nine-feet in length, the large creature met us at the front windows of the vessel, which came to a temporary halt. Its mouth opened wide as if it were readying itself to speak to us, when in fact it brought its powerful top and bottom jaws down over a large translucent yellow jellyfish for a delicious early-evening meal.

Then, its mouth opened to deliver the initial lessons we were to receive in this tiny yellow submarine on Gratitude.

I opened the book, depressed the yellow button at the tip of the pen and wrote the word GRATITUDE in yellow at the top of blank Page 11.

With the pen ready to glide yellow ink easily across the page, another surge of lemon aromatic mist spread throughout the cabin and entered easily into my heart space. I went into a mode of no-thought and no-doing, silently sitting and watching as the turtle eloquently spoke. The following phrases began to appear in mustard yellow on the paper of Page 12.

The Benefits of Gratitude

Gratitude improves emotional health

Gratitude boosts compassion and lessens anger

Gratitude improves the quality of sleep

Gratitude increases psychological strength

Gratitude increases spiritual strength

Gratitude boosts confidence

Gratitude sends you more of what you desire

Gratitude enriches one's self-worth

Gratitude launches the rocket of healthier
relationships
Gratitude increases physical health

I reviewed each line for its essence and accuracy and read them to Champo and the Sacred Elder. The large leatherback tortoise left us with this mystical message, "Slow down, you move too fast in your life. You miss the essence of the now, which is where Gratitude resides. When you are grateful for life, your heart opens wide, and the universe sends to you more of what you desire. Journey well, my friends."

The turtle swiftly turned its large frame and swam off to the left through a school of Nassau Grouper, who changed their green body color to yellow when the leatherback came through. The yellow swimmers encapsulated our boat and after easily pressing quietly through them the submarine dove further, leaving our nose angled downward at 45 degrees. The vessel stopped, giving us the perfect view inside the shells of three massive clams resting at the bottom of the ocean floor.

The Sacred Elder said, "With the recent teachings delivered to us by the turtle about the Benefits of Gratitude, let us reflect on them and observe on the three TV screens inside the clam shells about the wonders of gratitude and the ancient power it gives to the practitioner."

The clam on the left came to life and its shell lit up in a lemon yellow. The screen within it produced a random colored dot pixel pattern of static on the display and the speakers in our vessel produced its corresponding noise.

The static left the screen and the speakers and a video played showing parents with their two small children at a park playing Frisbee with wide contagious smiles across all of their faces. Their laughter came loudly over the speakers, bringing a sense of gratitude within the vessel.

The image froze and the middle clam came to life and its shell lit up in a lemon yellow color. The screen within it produced a pattern of static on the display and the speakers in our vessel produced its corresponding noise.

The static left the screen and the speakers and a video played showing a man standing at the brink where the sand meets the cool ocean water, while his outstretched arms project confidence and self-worth up to the stars. The loud ocean waves crashing to the shore came over the speakers in the boat with a feeling of peace along with it.

That second image froze and the right clam came to life and its shell lit up in a lemon yellow. The screen within it produced the pattern of static on the display and the speakers in our vessel produced its corresponding noise.

The static left the screen and the speakers and a video showed a group of meditation practitioners sitting in a circle and chanting Om Mani Padme Hum on their way toward spiritual awakening. The chanting came through the speakers and brought a stillness along with it.

The three screens with frozen images simultaneously went back to static and after a few moments went black. The yellow clam shells transformed back into their natural beige orange color and our boat brought itself out of the angled position and floated parallel with the ocean floor.

Einstein again called out, "Gratitude attracts, awk, Gratitude attracts."

The Sacred Elder continued, "Now we see some examples of how gratitude brings more happiness, joy, and what one desires to life. Gratitude means thanks and appreciation. An attitude of gratitude will usually determine your longitude and latitude in life."

The boat moved forward through the yellow-tinted waters and the captain came over the speakers, "Please be advised that there are rough waters ahead due to some underground volcanic activity. To avoid that space, we will be taking a detour to our right and will pass safely through two sunken pirate ships where several sharks are guarding the ships' lost and sunken treasure."

Our vessel safely entered the waters between the two somewhat illuminated massive brown sunken ships and stopped in the middle of them. Three great white sharks zig zagged among and over treasure chests resting on the ocean floor. Gold necklaces were strewn over the sides of the partially opened chests and several rubies, diamonds, sapphires, and gold coins sat reflecting in uneven piles, filling the space between the chests.

A deeply familiar and unique brogue accent came over the left and right speakers, "Yarr, there's no getting to my treasure Matey's! Come and see for yourself. The sharks will rip you to pieces and use you as bait for their dinner. There's no stealing this here treasure!"

Einstein stood perched atop Champo's right shoulder and was visibly shaking. He cried out, "Yarr Matey, awk, Yarr Matey," while continuing to tremble. The sharks came quickly to the windows of the boat and looked straight into it. Their large beautiful, yet scary, blue eyes were captivating and seemed to glow in the darkened underwaters.

It was their teeth that showed through the glass next, which brought a sense of terror through my spine. They gently rubbed their grey and white scales against the sides of the boat, which rocked and brought it closer to the sunken treasure. The propellors spun faster, lifted us higher, and again brought us to a 45-degree downward angle to view the ships, pirates, treasure, and great whites.

The distinctive pirate's voice entered our cabin once more and said, "Arr Matey! Too afraid to open the hatch and take a chance at the treasure? You and everyone else! Come back again soon when you've mustered up the courage. We'll be waiting for ya!"

The boat carried us forward at an angle to the left and we were clear of the danger. Einstein stopped shaking and the boat slowed as we approached several metal stanchions sticking out from the bottom of the ocean, protruding up through the surface of the water.

Champo said, "There is no turning back now. We have come too far. We are being blocked and challenged for a reason. Although it does seem that if the vessel maneuvered itself just right, we'd be able to make it through these tall shiny teetering columns."

Champo stood up, walked to the dashboard controls and flipped a yellow switch from the down autopilot to the up manual override position.

"I'm going to get us through the barriers. We must sit for a moment, as the vessel recalibrates itself into manual, and focus on the things in our lives we are grateful for," said Champo.

The boat made several mechanical clicking and switching noises as we sat contemplating those things in our lives we were grateful for. I knew Einstein was happy to be away from the scary sharks and truth be told, so was I.

Next to the switch to bring the boat into manual mode there was a black joystick that maneuvered the vessel. Champo took hold of it, brought us back 15 feet and practiced steering us through the yellow waters. He got the hang of it relatively quickly and moved us within the tall rocking pillars. It was a delicate dance between ship and pylon where one wrong maneuver would spell doom.

We swerved left, right, glided ahead and came to a huge white nylon banner stretched out between two posts twenty-feet apart. The large mustard yellow letters read "Life Barriers to Gratitude." I wrote that as the heading on Page 13 of my composition book and watched as the banner waved and rippled above us.

When we fully passed underneath it, a series of banners appeared ahead of us to the left and right with phrases spelled out in the same colored lettering across them. They were unique in that a single number showed at the bottom center of each sign and if we were going to make it through the posts successfully, we'd have to pass beneath them in the specific numerical order or start over at number 1.

The Sacred Elder stood at the left windows, I stood at the windows on the right and Champo steered us while looking through the front glass. "There's Number 1," cried the Sacred Elder.

Champo brought us in front of and slightly below the first banner, which had, "Feelings of envy," written across it. I wrote that phrase in the notebook.

"There's Number 2," said Champo, and he closed us in on the second banner, which read, "Feelings of resentment."

"Look off to our right, it's banner Number 3," I said. The boat easily reached it and I wrote, "Feelings of jealousy," on the next line.

We naturally found each banner and phrase in order and the rest of the banners, 4-8, read as follows:

Feelings of decreased energy
Feelings of cynicism
Feelings of entitlement
Feelings of greed
Displays of narcissism

Between the pirate ships, pirates, sunken treasure, sharks, and the wobbly pillars, we successfully made it through the "Life Barriers to Gratitude."

I read all eight of them out loud while Champo guided us back to open waters. Straight ahead, in the depths appeared a small uninhabited body of land on the ocean floor. Approximately one hundred and fifty feet in diameter, the small sandy beige mass had a large yellow pole sticking out from its center. The white sign with bright yellow letters running across read, "Lost City of Avalon."

Sitting in the sand and leaning up against the thick tall tree-like post was a giant life-like representation of Buddha. The Sacred Elder said, "We have come across The Lost City of Avalon and hover in this tiny craft before one of the greatest religious and mystical figures this world has known. Champo and I have heard of this lost city as part of the tales the Elders told us throughout time, and here we are. How very fortunate we are to have stumbled across both of these magnificent entities."

The large Buddha's eyes slowly opened and he yawned deep and long from being asleep for so many years. He fully came to and with outstretched hands he gestured and spoke at length to us, while we sat awestruck and listened intently.

"In Buddhism, we don't practice to attain anything; not enlightenment, good karma, a satisfactory rebirth, or materialistic rewards. We practice simply to give thanks for what we have already received. I come before you today to provide an ancient teaching on the Gratitude Mini-Chakra."

The Buddha appeared to take up the entire island and was a magnetic force of being. He continued to teach us, "The original location of the heart chakra was the center of the sternum. There is still an energy center there and it is referred to as the Gratitude Mini Chakra. The following ancient exercise will allow you to tap deeply into the well of gratitude within. Take the fingers of your dominant hand and tap on the bumps at your sternum this way."

The Buddha showed us light tapping with the tips of his right fingers at the center of his chest.

"Tap lightly on these bumps and repeat the words, 'I am grateful for life.' Keep tapping and repeat that phrase, 'I am grateful for life.' Take a deep breath in through your nose and blow it fully out of your mouth and again say, 'I am grateful for life.' Repeat the exercise, breaths, and phrase, three times only and stop. Notice what you feel. Do this exercise between three to twenty-seven times a day for one complete lunar cycle.

"When you think of something during the day that

you are grateful for, simply tap on those tiny bumps and repeat the phrase, 'I am grateful for life.' As an alternative, when you think of something you are grateful for in your life, place the palm of one hand over your heart and then the palm of the other hand over the top and repeat the phrase, 'I am grateful for life.'

"Remember, you are not practicing this exercise to attain anything. You are practicing it simply for the sake of letting the universe know how grateful you are for what you have already received in your life. Only then will you be sent more. That is not up to you, however. Practicing gratitude is."

The Buddha's arms floated down to his lap and rested there. A flood of gratitude washed over and through the boat and streamed like tiny sharp bolts of lightning through the three of us. Einstein jumped up and down on Champo's right shoulder and flew excitedly in small circles about the vessel.

A sharp alarm warning siren and flashing yellow strobe light initiated inside the boat. Next to the joystick, we observed on the small sonar screen, three blips approaching us from behind. Einstein landed on the left rubber black handle of the folded-up periscope and swung hanging upside down. He cried, "Not Again, awk, Not again," and sure enough the three Great White sharks raced from behind and caught up to us. They rammed their heads into the boat, knocking us out of balance.

The engine stopped from the collision and we slowly began to sink to the sand next to the Buddha. He opened his mouth, took in volumes of water, and blew it forcefully at the ravenous deep-sea carnivores. They appeared shaken and in their disorientated state swam hurriedly off, back to protect the pirates' loot.

The Buddha scooped our craft from the sandy bottom with his right hand and held us in its palm, while the Sacred Elder blew onto the yellow crystal between her right thumb and index finger. The engine sputtered, clearing out heaps of sand within its chambers, and finally stirred rhythmically. The sounds of whirring propellors were music to our ears.

The Buddha's voice came one last time over our speakers and told us, "Knowing the benefits and blockages to Gratitude is one thing. It is another thing to affirm and solidify its glorious effects within. Take these daily affirmations with you and remember to practice gratitude daily until it becomes not second, but first nature."

I opened the composition book to Page 14 and wrote "Daily Gratitude Affirmations" at the top center of the page.

The pen, with the same yellow ink, glided my hand across the page, jotting down the Seven Gratitude Affirmations of the Lost City of Avalon, as spoken by the great Buddha.

I am grateful for life
I am grateful for all the people in my life
I am grateful for everything I have in my life
I am grateful for my intuition, imagination,
  and dreams
I am grateful for my health
I am grateful to be able to do what I love
I am grateful for the inner workings of my
  physical body

"What a great opportunity we have had today to come across one another. For this I am truly honored and grateful. Pass delicately and safely through these waters and teach all you have learned about the first Four FLAGS to the people. You still have one more Flag to go and perhaps we will see one another again soon."

"And so it is," said the Sacred Elder.

We stood at the front window and bowed three times to the Buddha; he brought his palms together at the heights of his Gratitude Mini-Chakra and in a sitting lotus posture, bowed three times at us.

The boat sped off and faint auditory trails of, "Namasté friends," followed us in the waters from behind.

I depressed the yellow button on the pen and clipped it inside the notebook between Pages 14 and 15. I put them into my backpack, Champo flipped the switch back down to auto-pilot, and the three of us sat back down on the hard yellow plastic seating. We looked at each other and at the same time said, "What a ride!"

"Literally," I said. And we all laughed.

The vessel steadily rose to the surface of the water and realigned itself in front of the other boats at the dock from where we originally boarded. An air decompression hiss accompanied the opening of the pastel pink hatch at the top right side of the vessel. With Einstein on his right shoulder, Champo climbed out first, gave the Sacred Elder a hand, and I stayed behind for a moment.

I took a gradual visual impression of the submarine's innards, inhaled one last fresh lemon scent deeply into my lungs, and grounded my being into a still state of harmonious gratitude. *What an amazing life* I thought to myself as I blew all of the air out while climbing onto the wide grey beaten wood boards of the ancient dock.

Champo, Einstein, the Sacred Elder, and I joined in a circular embrace of gratitude on the platform. The hummingbirds and monarchs put the finishing touches on the huddle by hovering tightly above and around us, bringing the gratitude effect on full display.

Inside the warm embrace, the Sacred Elder reiterated, "Let us think for a moment about all the amazing effects practicing gratitude brings. How do you feel at this moment? Breathe it fully in and hold it for a few seconds. Now release gratitude out into the world. We will bring the important messages of gratitude to the people in order to have them go from a life of deep suffering to a life of blissful awakening."

CHAPTER SEVENTEEN

SURRENDER

Our warm gathering dispersed and our winged friends beckoned us to follow. We briskly walked across the air-dried clay grey brick pavers a few hundred yards to the entrance of a tall expanse of long horizontal white stone stairs. Hovering high above was the final wrought iron black arched sign we'd see this cool crisp earthy fall evening. In large, white, bold letters it read, "The Surrender House at Avalon Lake."

I looked at the massive edifice that stood before us, which reminded me of the beautiful Château d'Ussé, in Rigny-Ussé, France. The circular turrets and chimneys protruded skyward while the thousands of rectangular beige stones adorned the outer surface of the castle. Getting closer, we observed the northern side of the palace cleared away, allowing fine picturesque views across the terraces and man-made river. I recognized the yellow tinted waters from the Gratitude Geyser attraction we recently visited.

Standing at the base of a fifty-foot white stone staircase leading up to the structure, the butterflies and hummingbirds bid us farewell and we started our climb to the top front terrace. Champo and the Sacred Elder walked first and I followed closely behind, while Einstein flew up close-by.

Halfway up, we turned to take in the amazing views of the entire ancient mystical park. We observed each ride we experienced and noticed Avalon Island lit up in bright purple, blue, green, and yellow colors. I deeply inhaled the earthy smells of this fine magical autumn evening and we turned back to hold the railing to finish our steep climb.

When we reached the summit, Champo and the Sacred Elder embraced the black uniformed samurai who was guarding the two thirty-foot Cuban mahogany wood doors. In the center of each door at a six-feet high level, large round black wrought-iron knockers were mounted into the thick wood.

"This is David," said the Sacred Elder, who introduced me to the samurai.

We bowed three times to one another. He then grabbed his long wooden oak Bo Staff samurai stick leaning against the tall wooden door on the right and brought it forcefully down three times into the stone floor. At the third contact with the floor, a depressurized hissing sound initiated, which opened the massive wood doors inward.

Champo, the Sacred Elder, and I entered first, followed by Einstein and the samurai, who came in and slammed the Bo Staff into the tile one time, bringing the wooden doors to a soft gentle close.

"Please remove your shoes and follow me down the central corridor of the palace," instructed the samurai.

Einstein perched onto Champo's right shoulder and we followed the samurai single file in the same order we entered the building. Beautiful framed portraits of other grand castles and chateaus hung on the walls to the left and right of the high ceiling foyer.

Wrought-iron holders bolted into the stone walls were spaced out every ten feet at six-feet levels off the floor. Rod-like pieces of wood with flammable fluid-soaked white cloth were wrapped around the protruding flamed ends. The torches provided the needed light to guide us to the end of the corridor, where a fifty-foot high beige travertine stone wall greeted us.

We gathered in a half-moon semi-circle and watched as the samurai provided us with information regarding the symbols on the smooth tile wall before us. He stood with his back to the wall at a 45-degree angle and gestured with his right hand, pointing at the symbols and characters.

"Looking up, we can see the images of Five FLAGS. Within each flag you will find the word associated with the flag in its center. Forgiveness, Love, Acceptance, Gratitude, and Surrender, respectively. You have experienced the initial Four FLAGS on your journey thus far.

"Here, in the House of Surrender at Avalon Lake, we will gather in the ancient meditation hall behind me where we will study and learn about Surrender and the other Four FLAGS in greater depth in order to bring their understanding to the world. Please follow me."

I glanced up one final time at the images of the Five FLAGS on the wall and a deep well of gratitude came up through the floor, into my feet, and coursed through my entire being. The samurai turned, grabbed the slot in grey stone door with the four fingers of his right hand

and slid it to the left. The Great Meditation Hall appeared before us, and we walked in and up to the rectangular deep purple meditation cushions laid out in a circle.

We chose our cushions and sat down on the round black Zafu cushions atop the purple rectangular Zabuton. Three additional Scarlet Macaws flew through the opened doorway and landed on the right shoulders of me, the Sacred Elder, and the samurai.

From Champo's right shoulder, Einstein let out three high-pitched whistles and screamed, "Welcome friends, awk, welcome friends."

The samurai lit three sandalwood incense sticks and placed the stems down through holes of an antiquated white stone holder. The exotic, sweet, creamy, smooth, and warm scent enveloped us and prompted the Sacred Elder to begin.

"The sacred burnt ash from the Hyperion tree is now going to be blown out from my cupped palms into the shared circle before us. Breathe in the ash and allow it to open your third-eye chakra. With this opening, focus on your deep inhalations and exhalations, while bringing all of your attention there. Allow stillness, presence, and conscious awareness to connect us. Step into the understanding that there is no place that one of us begins and the other ends. We are now connected as one single unit."

We breathed in the ash, opened our third eyes, and sensed the unification.

The Sacred Elder continued, "We will be spending time here together as a team of four to learn the Laws of Avalon and The Five FLAGS of Transformation, yet there is one more who is destined to join us and complete our Infinity Team of Five. This fifth member is not yet among us, and is currently searching to find you, David. For now, I will come around and place the tip of my right index finger at each of your third-eye chakra points to have a wider, deeper, shared unified opening."

The Sacred Elder arose from her cushion and one by one, made contact between our eyes with the soft tip of her right index finger. She remained a bit longer kneeling in front of me and added a little bit of the burnt grey ash of the Hyperion tree to the spot. Her soft whispering of "Om Mani Padme Hum" produced a wonderful relaxation in my heart as did her translation of it: "The jewel is in the lotus and the lotus is deep within you."

The chanting continued. The incense burned. The four Scarlet Macaws bounced on our shoulders, lifted off and encircled us from ten-feet above. The energy in the large meditation hall was palpable and the index finger at my forehead began tapping softly and rhythmically with the humming.

The Sacred Elder took her seat and said, "For the conclusion of our experience today learning about The Five FLAGS of Transformation, I will be channeling all of the information regarding the final Flag of Surrender. There will be no need to take notes, for this last piece will imbed itself mystically in the places that matter within each of us. Let's remember to keep our cups empty in order to fully experience the scope and elements of the sacred art of Surrender."

The upward spiraling thin lines of sandalwood smoke heightened our presence and we each placed the palms of both hands face up resting on our knees. The Sacred Elder instructed us to open our eyes slightly and bring our gaze to her. She took a small orange crystal from her leather pouch, rested it on the palm of her left hand, and poured a fine helping of grey Hyperion ash over it. Taking a nice inhale, she blew the air forcefully from her lungs across the ash and stone, into the circular space before us.

The ash formed a mostly translucent screen made up of tiny orange dust sparkles. The screen rotated slowly in front of us and took on a holographic appearance. The bold capitalized black letters appeared into the middle of the screen, reading, "SURRENDER." I went to reach for the composition book and multi-colored pen nestled in my backpack and remembered it was not necessary.

The Sacred Elder said, "The remaining orange color and fragrance about to enter this domain corresponds to the final lesson of Surrender. Right now, it is useful to ponder on how surrendering can bring peace to your life and can help you consciously manifest a happy one. Surrendering to a higher power or the universe may sound a bit scary or daunting at times, but as you release control, a newfound sense of ease, peace, and aliveness comes to life."

The Sacred Elder poured one more simple coat of grey matter onto the orange crystal and blew, initiating a surge of powerful orange zest into the vicinity. Initially, I felt a calm come over me; my tight shoulders relaxed a couple of inches from their customary raised posture. I felt an abundance of warmth and renewed energy envelop me as we propelled deeper into the surrendered state.

The room took on a pumpkin glow. I looked up at Einstein and his feathers were now completely accented with the colors purple, blue, green, yellow, and orange. He remained on Champo's right shoulder and basked in the warm orange glow. The Sacred Elder's dress remained snow white and her hair was now perfectly rainbow-streaked in a combination of purple, blue, green, yellow, and orange, reminiscent of the colors of The Five FLAGS.

She said, "The origin of oranges is the Southeast Himalayan foothills, where many of our friends reside. It has been used for over 7,000 years for its healing color and fragrant properties toward the spiritual act of surrender, by opening and healing the original fifth sacral "surrender" chakra located an inch and a half below the belly button and two inches within. With the opening of the surrender chakra, greater access and understanding into the releasing of control and attainment of joy are found."

The four Scarlet Macaws obviously adored what was just said because they bounced up and down on our shoulders and collectively uttered, "Surrender the Ego, awk, Surrender the Ego."

"That's right friends," said the Sacred Elder. "While we learn and embody the sacred topic of surrender, remember that if you think you already know, attempt to control, get caught up in the illusions of memories and anticipations, surrender will be kept at bay and a life of friction and resistance will continue."

The word SURRENDER remained spinning in the center of the orange holographic projection and we were reminded that, "Surrender reveals to us the 'isness' of this present moment. Let's continue to remember ourselves and that sacred part within that has the ability to grow. In turn, the lessons of surrender will deepen and ultimately we will bring them to the world. Here and now we will learn how to surrender what weighs us down, so we may take flight like our friends who sit upon our shoulders."

For the next several minutes we sat motionless within the orange room and focused on our ancient breathing awareness technique. The refreshing orange scent reminded me of summer barbeques at our home at the ocean shores of my youth.

The Sacred Elder sensed I was caught up in a memory and pointed an inch and a half long clear crystal at me. The thin beam of white light caught my attention, instantly brought me back to the present moment, and another burst of orange zest spread through my solar plexus, sacral, and root chakras. I fully entered into a still form of no-thought and no-doing.

She took the beam of white light off me and carried it over to the rotating orange screen. The word SURRENDER evaporated and the Sacred Elder magically scribed the following insightful phrases on the auburn backdrop:

The Benefits of Surrender
Surrender helps us get creative
Surrender fosters emotional freedom
Surrender initiates positive energy
Surrender brings a sense of inner peace
Surrender promotes greater joy and happiness
Surrender opens doors where there once were walls
Surrender boosts the immune system

Surrender facilitates goal attainment

Surrender introduces heightened physical, emo-
tional, and spiritual well-being

The Sacred Elder said, "David, please read each phrase that appears on the rotating screen."

I read each line, which had the benefits of surrender instilled deeper within my sacral, solar plexus, and root chakras.

She continued, "Now, let us all think for a moment about the miracles of surrender. Now that we have observed and learned these phrases on the screen before us, what do you sense the practice of surrender can do for you and others? Let's watch together and we'll see the power surrender unleashes."

The Sacred Elder put the orange fire agate stone between the thumb and index finger of her left hand and holding both crystals in her outstretched hands, whizzed them through the air. Vigorous bolts of orange and white lightning coursed wildly and mixed through the middle of the screen.

A vivid and colorful scene emerged depicting a swarm of seagulls circling tightly in a thermal above the ocean shore. We heard the waves crashing, as the next image revealed a child running freely and openly through a park chasing after a kaleidoscope of monarch butterflies. The child sat on the luscious dew-filled grass, extended her right arm out and seven butterflies landed upon her outstretched arm.

The next scene showed a young man and woman lying on an orange and white blanket meditating at the beach, while inhaling the ocean waves deeply into their lungs and exhaling them back out into the wider sea. Then, a monstrous mountain range emerged and at the summit, a young woman sat with her feet dangling off the edge of the cliff, while she stared out in wonder and amazement at life.

A group of hot-air balloon enthusiasts, fastened to the ground, simultaneously untethered their ropes and rose together buoyantly into the ether.

The final scene on the orange screen demonstrated a happily married couple celebrating their 25th wedding anniversary riding horseback at sundown on the powdery white sandy beaches of Florida's Emerald Coast. As the brown and black horses trotted slowly side by side through the powdery sand, the couple turned their faces, gazed deeply into each other's eyes, and fell madly in love once again.

The delightful images slowly faded from the screen and the Sacred Elder said, "We see how surrender brings more creativity, freedom, and energy to life. Surrender means letting go and arriving at the flow of harmony within the natural laws of the universe. It implies entering the present moment, which is the death of the Ego."

Something unknown, unheard, and unobservable startled the four Sacred Macaws and they all flew off, including Einstein, onto a tall wide stone perch approximately twenty yards from our circle. The Sacred Elder flew her hands across the screen once more and the phrase, "Symptoms of Unhealthy Control" appeared in large bold white letters on the orange backdrop. Following that slogan one by one were the symptoms themselves.

Symptoms of Unhealthy Control
Lack of trust
Increased anxiety
Fear of abandonment
Low self esteem
Fear of failure

Need to micromanage

Fear of experiencing painful emotions

Einstein and his three new friends flew back onto our right shoulders and the Sacred Elder brought her dancing arms down to rest on her lap. She asked the samurai to read each of the phrases that just appeared, and he did so slowly and with purpose, which had the understanding of unhealthy control instilled deeper within us.

"Now," she continued, "Let us think for a moment about all the amazing effects practicing surrender brings. How about the billions of people on the planet who are strapped in an unhealthy, non-surrender, controlled life. They are not at least, free, or filled with increased energy. It's enough to cause the multitude of physical, emotional, and spiritual sicknesses and diseases we currently witness.

"We will bring the important messages of surrender to the people in order to have them go from a life of control to a life of harmonious flow and self-expression."

The Sacred Elder now asked the samurai to stand

and grab his Bo Stick that leaned up against the wall by the door we entered. He grabbed it and remained standing tall and erect behind his meditation cushions. He knew exactly what to do from here, because he has sat and trained together many times prior.

He grasped the long thin dark wood at approximately six-inches from either end with both hands and mystically whirled it in place. A white light appeared overhead as he raised the staff, creating a continuous circle above him. The orange sign before us changed to solid white and beautiful images, with their accompanying sounds of majestic waterfalls emerged at the left and right margins of the screen.

The samurai slowed his whirl, performed various Aikido movements with the long stick, and stood still once more behind his cushions, with the staff held tightly across his chest at a 45-degree angle.

The Sacred Elder thanked him and motioned with her outstretched right arm to sit once more. She produced the clear crystal between her right thumb and index finger and drew letters in the air from her cushions between the waterfalls. The following appeared on the screen for 10 seconds apiece and then morphed into the next phrase.

Surrender Affirmations

I let go of what I cannot change

I am taken care of regardless of the outcome

*I am open and willing to experience my life in
    new ways*

The universe has a grander plan than I do

When I simply let go I grow

I relax and therefore enjoy life

I continually surrender my expectations of others

I am the calm within the storm

Setbacks jolt me into new awareness

I release the desire to make others wrong

I am ready and happy for miracles to enter my life

At any moment I can choose to be peaceful

Champo took his hands and with the right fingertips on top of and touching his left fingertips below, he
slowly drew his right hand higher above the left and increased the size of the white screen in the circle. This
enlarged the waterfalls and allowed all 12 Surrender Affirmations to be on the screen at once.

The phrases remained in the middle while the two
magnificent and robust waterfalls, along with their pic-

turesque pool-plunges at the bottom, remained on the side screens. The sounds of the falling and crashing white water foam brought an even greater sense of surrender and tranquility over us.

The Sacred Elder nodded at Champo who said, "What a great opportunity we have to surrender that which we have no control over. We will bring and teach this life-altering and transformational practice to the people along with the other Four FLAGS."

"And so it is," said the Sacred Elder. "I want you all to sit in contemplation of Surrender as I summon an ancient friend from another world to speak with us further on the topic. He is not known in this world and his name does not translate into a dialect of earth. Clucking and clicking sounds made with his tongue is his language and I will interpret the sounds into English for us to understand his wisdom."

The phrases left the screen and the waterfalls and pool-plunges stayed. The audio turned off and the same static appearance as within the three large clam shells appeared. The Sacred Elder said, "Testing. Testing 1, 2," which produced a fluctuation wave pattern within the static each time she spoke.

In her long bright white gown and multi-colored hair, sitting atop the round black cushion, she closed her eyes, held two clear crystals in the grasp of either hand, and waited for her friend to channel through.

We heard faint clicks and they spaced out more and became more pronounced. On the static monitor, every click produced a black hole within it. After approximately 30 seconds of this, the Sacred Elder began to translate.

"Hello again, my dear friend. How wonderful it is to be with you and your friends today — for you and no day for me. Where I reside, recall there is no time and we exist in a much simpler Egoless fashion. Let me remind you, I come with no Ego and from a state of no competition. Please, temporarily turn off your ego-mind if it is still on.

"I was a frequent visitor to the land you currently sit at and when all of the people stopped coming, the Ego grew individually and collectively. My services were no longer required. This Adventure Museum must open again. Champo, Sacred Elder, Samurai, and David, you four will teach the concepts learned today along with the following information.

"Instead of the ego-self thinking, 'I can fix this,' teach the people to be willing to immerse their perceived problem into their deeper selves. For those in your audience who grew up believing life is a 'do-it-yourself' project, for them it will be hard to admit they need help merely to survive.

"Like the ripple at the top of an ocean wave, separated from its source, the tiny mind is unable to create and sustain full life. But when the ripple at the top of the ocean wave rejoins the larger ocean it has all the powers of its source. The ripple separate from its source symbolizes the ego-self, when one is separated from the one source of our source of omnipotent Universal Intelligence.

"With our celestial connection we are always in touch with the solutions we are seeking. The Ego creates problems which persist when we fail to recognize, realize, and quietly connect with our own deep awareness within.

"When faced with seemingly impossible problems, I often suggest to the person, 'Try to surrender to your source and turn this problem over to that same power that rotates the planets. Turn your worries over to that power that animates the entire universe.'

"When you practice connecting silently with spirit, you will sense the presence of a sacred partner deep within you. You may eventually feel as if that presence is you. Initially though, surrender your problems to this re-source and naturally move to a place of peace. Eventually, you will learn that all those so-called 'problems' are dissolvable by soaking them with the deeper energies of consciousness.

"Thank you friends, for allowing me to be with you briefly today. Please continue bringing these ancient messages to the people. They need them more now than ever. Peace be with you."

We each raised our hands up palms together, and bowed several times.

The Sacred Elder opened her eyes, joined the two clear crystals together, and pointed them at the center of the screen between the waterfalls. Large black bold letters appeared and spelled out, *The Five FLAGS of Transformation.*

The Sacred Elder continued, "The FLAGS is an acronym for the Tunnel, rides, and current House of Surrender we currently sit in at The Amusement Park at Avalon Lake. Forgiveness, Love, Acceptance, Gratitude, and **S**urrender are the lessons, teachings, signposts, and affirmations etched into the composition book and our hearts and minds. Soon, once the Infinity Team of five is completed, we will spend time elaborating on and bringing them to various cities around the world to teach people.

Please recall, surrender is that sacred place where Forgiveness, Love, Acceptance, and Gratitude converge. When we merge the Five **FLAGS** of Transformation together with being okay not knowing what's next, sacred stillness and conscious action evolves."

The Sacred Elder finished speaking and nodded to Champo, who placed the middle and index fingers of his right hand under his tongue and blew a loud piercing whistle, prompting the four Scarlet Macaws to lift off our right shoulders and fly in a wide circle thirty-feet above us.

They took turns letting out exacting guttural squawks and growls, as if summoning a great mystical force into the massive stone meditation hall. The Sacred Elder retracted the crystals in a reverse corkscrew fashion through the air and the screen disappeared.

CHAPTER EIGHTEEN

THE FINAL CLIMB

A loud grumbling and rumbling came from the center of the wide circle and what appeared like the ground caving in before us, was in fact a massive Hyperion tree coming forcefully and rapidly through the floor and eventually bursting through the one-hundred-foot ceiling above us. All the concrete and stone debris fell behind us and the Sacred Elder instructed us to stack the cushions by the wall and then go quickly to the door from which we entered and put on our shoes.

Once the tree was completely through the ceiling, we returned to the circle and entered the tree at its base, through a large arched opening.

We walked to the center of the hulled-out inside and I was taken by the aromatic mild spice with earthy undertone sweetness. There was a dry wood quality about this natural canopy and single file, we lined up at wood rungs spread out on top of one another every one and a half feet at one specific spot on the wall.

The samurai climbed first and the top and bottom of his Bo Staff clanked each time he went up a rung. The Sacred Elder brought the bottom of her white gown through her legs and managed to twist and tie it into makeshift shorts. She followed the samurai, I went next, and Champo was last to climb.

The four Scarlet Macaws were already at the top waiting for us, perched on a wooden platform. We were already a few minutes in and working up a healthy per-spiration. We couldn't afford to take a hand off the wood handles to wipe the accumulated sweat from our soaked faces. The rungs became slippery nonetheless, which warranted and produced heightened awareness, focus, and concentration.

Half-way up, there was an opening to the right of the wood grips with a large wide branch to climb out on but we chose to bypass it completely and make it in one fell swoop to the summit. Three quarters of the way up the Sacred Elder lost the grip with her right hand and connected with the top of my dome with her left foot. "Sorry!" she called out and I replied, "Thanks, I needed that!" Actually it helped me focus my attention on each rung of the ladder up.

We were moving at a healthy rhythmic clip and the Sacred Elder told us, "Bring all of your awareness to the feeling your palms have when grasping the wood handles. Also, bring your attention to the space between the rungs and there you will find stillness."

This is precisely what we needed to hear. Our movements were exact. Right hand grip and left foot climb. Left hand grip and right foot climb. We must have looked like a centipede to the birds above who patiently waited our arrival.

The samurai exited out of the top first and stood on the wood platform. Then the Sacred Elder grabbed the samurai's outstretched right hand and lifted out. They both offered hands and I grabbed them with each of mine while standing on the third rung from the top and they lifted me up out onto the thick sturdy wood platform. Champo was last. He grabbed the last rung with both hands, pushed his feet off the rung he stood on, and flipped forward, propelling himself upwards and out onto the wood expanse.

The samurai said, "Very funny, wise guy. Don't do

that again huh?" and we all laughed deeply while looking out at the clouds below us. We saw nothing else but clouds and a few mountain peaks. No amusement park in sight, just white puffy cumulus cotton balls.

The Sacred Elder said, "Over to our left, at the end of this ledge is the beginning of a spiral slide we will individually take down to the bottom. There we shall gather and make our way back to the stone stumps at the front of my stone house. It will take some time to make it to the bottom of the tree and it is not a competitive race. It is a creative endeavor for us always. Each one here will support the others in realizing their sacred aim of growth and expansion.

"Your respective Scarlet Macaw will fly in a corkscrew alongside you the entire slide down. Do not stop, yet stay present and aware at all times. Also, keep your eyes open. You never know what you might see. I will be with you at the top of the slide and as you put your feet out in front of you, I will be tapping grey ash onto your third-eye chakra. This will open the experience up for you. Take note of what you see and what happens within you as you pass through the clouds. Something sacred occurs at that point."

The samurai sent his Bo Stick first, the Sacred Elder tapped on his forehead, and he began his spiral slide down. We heard him shout out in excitement as Champo sat down. Einstein hovered a few feet in front of him as the tip of the Sacred Elder's right index finger danced on the skin between his eyes. He pushed off the platform and yelled out, "Yahoo," followed by Einstein's echoing, "Yahoo, awk, Yahoo."

I took my position at the top of the slide. With my backpack fully secured and my Scarlet Macaw patiently hovering, the Sacred Elder said, "What a magical journey you have endured today. Remember to make a mental note of what happens within you as you pass through the cloud cover. Who you are now, will more than likely not be the same person who comes out below the white fluffy masses. See you soon."

CHAPTER NINETEEN

PRESENT MOMENT LUCIDITY

She rubbed ash into my third-eye chakra and tapped with purpose at the same point. "Now," she said, and I propelled myself out onto the smooth light and dark wavy grains of the wooden slide. Around the first bend, everything slowed down and as I gazed off to my right at the Scarlet Macaw, its wing-flapping decelerated as did my glide. I took a deep breath in through my nose, held it for what seemed like forever within the base of my abdomen, and let it slowly out of my mouth.

Round and round I slid and the white cloud floor formation came closer toward me. *When will I break through?* I wondered and the Macaw scream brought me back to the moment and away from the wondering. The space between my eyes pulsated as if there was still a gentle tapping occurring. Then came the clouds.

One revolution, two revolutions, and as I sank deeper

into the white cloud cover, the voice inside my head said, "Wake up son, wake up." I saw the Scarlet Macaw still flying with me inside the puffy white and smelled the rich moist musty odor of a rainstorm brewing.

I broke through the bottom of the clouds and the, "Wake up son, wake up continued." The tapping became stronger on my forehead and I felt someone's hand grasping and shaking my left shoulder.

My eyes regained their focus from the dizzying white and standing above me was the ticket collector of the commuter train I boarded late this afternoon into Manhattan.

"That was some dream you were having, son. Everyone else got off five minutes ago and I've been trying to wake you up ever since. Let's get a move-on, I have to get this train cleaned and ready for the next load of passengers."

I rubbed my eyes and asked him, "Where am I?"

"You're at Grand Central Station son. You just completed the forty-five minute train ride into New York City."

I fully came to, sat up in my seat, and shook my head from side to side trying to get the mild spicy Hyperion fragrance out of my head.

"Can I have your ticket please?"

I reached into my left front pants pocket and produced the red ticket for the well-dressed man adorning the familiar ginger handlebar moustache. He took it, hole punched it, and said, "Have yourself a great day."

"You do the same pal," I said.

I zipped my backpack up, threw it over my right shoulder, and got off the train. I still felt as if I were in the dream I just had and wondered if I was perhaps now in a dream within another dream. There was one way to find out.

I walked quickly through several underground white subway tiled maze walkways and finally came outside to street level. A familiar scent wafted in the air as I observed the clean buildings, streets, and hordes of city-folk hurriedly walking and running to their next meeting. I followed the smell, like a dog tracking its favorite scent, to the bagel shop around the corner of the station. The malt, the steam, the oven all merged to create the aroma that had drew me in.

"Next," cried the white-aproned older lady behind the counter.

"Yes, I'll have an everything bagel with a shmear of plain cream cheese, a slice of raw onion, capers, and lettuce."

"You got it babe."

I paid for my food, put it in my backpack, exited the steamy room, and walked through Bryant Park. The lush gardens, outdoor chess matches, yo-yo demonstrations, outdoor cafes, and children playing, all enticed me to stay and people watch. I just didn't have the luxury but seeing and listening to all of the activities surrounding me, filled me with the needed energy to make it to my seminar at the Javits Center on time.

CHAPTER TWENTY
THE SEMINAR

My watch read 6:05pm. I exited Bryant Park at the southwest corner, hooked up with 6th Avenue, and then W. 38th Street. I walked through the Garment District and quickly took in the sights and sounds from the many factories and showrooms that were designing, manufacturing, and distributing clothing to the world. I saw hordes of vehicles entering and exiting Lincoln Tunnel on my right, bringing people to and from New Jersey.

I took a sharp left on 11th Avenue and was greeted by the massive glass-encased facade of the Javits Center. Another wave of excitement came over me as I grabbed a shiny horizontal door handle and pushed my way in.

I found a black faux leather bench in the foyer, placed my backpack down, and removed the prized baked possession. I took a bite into the warm aromatic seeded bagel and knew I wasn't dreaming any longer when the perfect combination of dough, cream cheese, capers, and onion merged in my saliva-laden mouth.

I quickly finished my meal, grabbed my backpack, threw the plastic container into the blue recycle bin, and walked over to the digital information board to locate my event. The personal-growth seminar started in five minutes and the location was listed as Meeting Room 1A03. I followed the signs, took the escalator up to the concourse level, which landed me right in front of my seminar room.

I walked to the registration tables and could already hear the hustle, bustle, and buzzing coming through the closed doors of the theater. Electronic Dance Music made the closed doors pulsate in rhythm and every fifteen seconds when the beat dropped, chants of, "Hey, hey, hey, hey," came from the enthusiastic crowd.

I could not wait to get in, find my reserved seat, and join in the pre-game frenzy. My turn in line came and the young man behind the black table-clothed rectangular banquet table asked me, "Can I see your I.D. please?"

I showed him my driver's license and he scrolled down the list of attendees, which was several pages long.

He stopped his index finger at my name, handed me back my ID and said, "You have been reserved a seat in the front row middle VIP section. I was instructed to escort you there myself when you arrived. The first speaker is about to take the stage so let's get you up there tout suite!"

I chose to not say a word and simply went with this easy flow, following him through the hallway leading up to the entrance door to the front-row seats by the stage. He opened the door to the theater and I was pulled in by the magnetism of the electrifying music and enthusiasm of the crowd. As he brought me to my seat I looked around the theater and noticed every seat was already taken.

"Thanks so much," I said to my escort and handed him some cash.

"Keep it," he said and hurriedly walked off.

I placed my backpack under the seat and said hello to the people to the right and left of me. They said hello back and then the entire place went black. The music continued to fill the space and I felt the loud bass as it connected to the rhythm of my beating heart. The beat dropped and shouts of, "Hey, hey, hey, hey filled the room once more.

Many people illuminated their cell phone flashlights and it was wild to see the thunderous free-flow dancing along with the swirling of their bright lights above their heads. After a couple of minutes of dancing with the crowd, I chose to sit down and quiet my busy mind, which had already wandered off to the waterfall and plunge-pool in my dream.

I took several deep breaths and rooted myself to the present moment, readying myself for the first speaker. That's when a familiar feeling came over me, as though there were others in the room I intimately knew. I didn't think much of it, I simply felt it, and breathed that feeling deep within, as I continued to ground myself to the now moment.

I placed my palms face up on my knees and took a visual impression of the entire room. People dancing, lights flashing, stage, carpet, chairs. I brought all of it up through the bottoms of my feet and became one with the energy of it all. Then a bright white spotlight was turned on, creating a large fifteen-foot white circle at the front center of the stage.

A voice from behind the curtains at the back of the stage said, "Ladies and gentlemen, as you take your seats, please turn off your cell phone lights and silence them."

A single loud drum bang came violently over the speakers and one-fifth of the white circle on stage filled with a purple hue. Then, a second loud drum sounded over the speakers and the next one-fifth of the white circle filled with a blue hue. The crowd was going absolutely nuts and I became quite curious. The next forceful drum beat came and another one-fifth of the white circle filled with pine green. The final two drum bangs came and the two remaining spots on the white circle filled with yellow, and orange respectively.

A wave of sweat and a little bit of panic came over me because they were the exact colors representing The Five FLAGS of Transformation in my recent dream. I felt nauseated and went into mild state of shock and disbelief. The sweat increased and I truly wondered if I was in fact still in a dream within the other dream. I pinched myself a few times and the girl to my left looked over and asked, "Hey are you okay?"

"Yeah, thanks, I'm fine," I replied. Even though I really wasn't.

It was hard to pull myself out and simply let go and

relax. Then the voice of Champo spoke through me, "Remember David, you must be okay not knowing."

That immediately relaxed me and I let the distracting and controlling thoughts go. I brought my attention to and became one with the sounds of the drum beating faster and when it hit its wonderful crescendo, the entire place became still and silent, as the gigantic black curtain soared upward.

The voice off stage said, "Are you ready?" and the crowd shouted "YES!"

"We cannot hear you. Are you ready?"

"Yes! Yes! Yes!"

The drum beat came back and the first speaker walked purposefully and slowly right into the center of the colored disc on the stage. Part of me told another part to faint but the stillness that was generated prior, when I became okay not knowing, prevented that from happening. Instead, I was filled with emotional joy and happiness, seeing Champo within that circle.

He looked right over to and made exacting eye contact with me. Staring right into my eyes he said, "Good to see you again!" Again the crowd stood and went wild, thinking he was speaking to each one separately.

"Please, please, take your seats. My name is Champo and you are in store for a crazy fun ride this weekend. Are you ready? And in 3, 2, 1, ..."

The lights went dark again except for the multi-colored circle and another small white spotlight that shined where the top of the curtain met the ceiling. A white banner released and the white spotlight caught it perfectly. It read **THE FIVE FLAGS OF TRANSFORMATION** in big bold black lettering.

It's not possible, I thought, and remembered that anything in fact is possible when one uses their sacred imagination and internal vision.

I turned to the girl sitting on my right and said, "Can you actually pinch my arm please?" She looked at me, smiled, and said, "I'd be happy to. I'm in shock right now too. I've waited forever to see them live." Then she pinched me.

"I guess it isn't a dream after all," I said to her.

"How can you be so sure? You're familiar with the song;

Row, row, row your boat
Gently down the stream
Merrily merrily, merrily, merrily
Life is but a dream

I simply nodded to her and brought my attention to Champo.

He continued, "Friends, relax into your seat and breathe deeply. Become aware of the consciousness within you and recognize that same energy in the people surrounding you. We are all connected. It is the subtle work of the Ego which attempts to convince us otherwise. Remember your intention for this weekend and set your aim right here and now. Bring a sense of sincerity to it and sprinkle some being into your doing this weekend. We gather together in co-creation, not competition."

As much as I wanted to believe this was actually happening and with all the energy I was placing on no-thought and being okay not knowing, my mind simply could not wrap itself around the fact that one of the characters from my dream was on stage standing within the familiar multi-colors of the pen I had used. He looked into my eyes again, this time locking onto them.

"This weekend, we bring you the ancient mystical teachings of The Five FLAGS of Transformation, providing you with all of the necessary tools and techniques to foster Forgiveness, Love, Acceptance, Gratitude, and Surrender in your life."

He pointed the index finger of his right hand at me and said, "Please allow me to introduce *YOU* to our first speaker of the evening. She is a globetrotting mystical warrior who brings ancient sacred knowledge from a variety of traditions, both known and unknown, to audiences far and wide. It is with great honor, pleasure, and sincerity that I introduce to you a being who truly knows what it means to be human."

The place went mad, pounding their heels on the floor and clapping their hands to the beat of the drum which had started back up. Everyone rose out of their seats and continued stomping, clapping, and screaming wildly. Champo finished, "May I introduce to you, the one and only, Miriam."

The venue went pitch black. The only light that remained illuminated was the small purple piece of the pie on stage. After a few moments, a silhouette gently strolled out and stood at the tip of the purple piece, at the previous center of the circle. The entire wheel illuminated once again and this time it glowed in a soft lavender.

A gentle white spotlight lit from the back of the theater and illustrated Miriam, who to me was affectionately known as the Sacred Elder from my dream.

She was dressed in a beautiful long white gown and her white hair was adorned with thin streaks of lavender. She scanned the crowd and motioned with her hands for us to sit back down. I could not sit down in her presence and therefore remained standing.

Noticing me, she walked toward the edge of the stage, raised her right hand, and motioned for me to walk over. I felt the hundreds of pairs of eyes on my back but remembered we were all one and therefore it did not faze me. I was only interested in being face-to-face with this sacred essence from my dream.

I walked up to her and she knelt down so we were eye-level. She pressed the mute button on the small black microphone control box clipped to the thin brown rope at her left waist. At the opposite side of the belt, I caught a glimpse of a leather pouch with two strings tied to the same rope.

She took my right hand in her left and whispered into my ear, "This one is not a dream but it is imperative that you recall all we shared with you and all you experienced. There is much work for us to do in order to bring the teachings and lessons of The Five FLAGS of Transformation to humanity. There is more a team of five people can do than a team of three or four. Look over my left shoulder off stage."

I looked and saw the samurai standing with his arms crossed looking straight ahead to the other side of the stage. I looked back at the Sacred Elder, who was untying the strings of the leather pouch. She removed a pinch of ash and rubbed it into the chakra of my third eye. She then disconnected the pouch from her waist, tied the two strings, and placed it in my right hand.

I closed my fingers tightly around the bag and said, "Thank you."

"Guard it well, share none of today's events with anyone, and we will be in contact very soon. I must begin for the audience. You already know the material of this seminar so there is no need for you to remain. There's actually quite a bit of work ahead of you to prepare. Any questions?"

I had thousands and knew they'd be answered in due time. For now, she had a seminar to lead and I was searching for the most prominent and useful question to ask before I left.

"You mentioned a team of five. Are you saying that I ...?"

"Yes, David. You will become one of the team soon, if you so choose. Then there will be another who will soon find you and they will complete the Infinity Team. This has been written in the cosmos for many millennia. Go now. Take your backpack and we will be together soon."

"Thank you," I whispered gently into her right ear and a single tear of joy came from the inner corner of my right eye down to my lips.

I put the leather pouch in my front right pants pocket, brought my palms together and bowed three times to her. She leaned forward, gave me a kiss on the left cheek, stood up and walked back to the center of the lavender circle. I looked over to the samurai, stage left, and Champo, stage right, and the three of us nodded in approval simultaneously. I took one final glance at the beautiful essence in white and grabbed my backpack from under my seat.

I walked towards the exit door of the theater and several people commented, "Way to go," "Good for you," and "Right on!" The attendant opened the door for me and before walking through it I turned back, took an impression of the stage and its surroundings, drew air deeply within my lungs, and exited the theater feeling incredibly grateful.

I walked briskly up the hallway and heard her voice speaking to the audience behind me. I went through the door by the registration tables and the guy who ushered me to my seat said, "Have a great night, David."

"Thanks so much!" I replied.

CHAPTER TWENTY ONE
THE CONCLUSION

I didn't mind missing her talk this evening, for my day was already full and complete. I exited the Javits Center and walked back down West 36th Street. The city was noisy, bright, and felt incredibly alive. I hooked a left onto 6th Avenue and walked energetically back into Bryant Park through the same Southwest corner I had exited before. I found an outside table at the Bryant Park Café and set my backpack down on the black wrought-iron seat next to me.

A cheery server came over and I ordered a decaf almond milk latte with three shots of expresso. I then set my sights on the bright glowing stars within the dark black sky up above.

The latte was the perfect temperature, had small wisps of vanilla tones, and hit the right spot deep within my abdomen.

A small parade of children, dressed in a variety of Halloween costumes, came through the café with their parents followed by three teenagers, most likely siblings of the costumed kids. The teens were playing an assortment of spooky Halloween tunes on an accordion, saxophone, and trumpet. Several café patrons dropped coins into their silver metal bucket hanging by a rope over the accordion player's neck as they walked by our tables.

I reached into my backpack, took out my baseball cap, and placed it on my head. My eyes were feeling heavy from the long day at work, the train ride into Grand Central, attending the seminar, and walking through Manhattan. Plus the dream on the train ride into the City, seeing Champo, the Sacred Elder, and the samurai, was another added emotional layer on top of everything.

I knew a short nap wouldn't hurt and I'd end up taking the late train from Grand Central back to my hometown station. I pulled the brim of the cap half-way over my eyes, dropped my chin slightly toward my chest, and dozed off to the fading sounds of spooky music, helicopters whizzing above, and café patrons discussing their lives.

The next thing I knew, someone was shaking me and tapping on my left shoulder. *It had to be the café server,* I thought as I quickly came to.

"Wake up David! David wake up. You're going to be late. C'mon David."

I raised my head up off my purple foam yoga mat and saw Audrey, my store manager, standing over me, pleading with me to wake up in the back storage room of my store.

"What's up, Audrey?"

"David, you've been out cold lying flat on your back here in the storage room for two hours. I tried calling back several times but you didn't answer and I was too busy with customers the entire afternoon to come back and wake you. If you hurry, you'll be able to make your seminar in time but you'll have to drive into Manhattan and forgo the train."

I rubbed my eyes, went into a backbend and heard several vertebral audibles as I stretched. I yawned deeply, stood up straight, and rolled up my foam mat.

"Audrey, you'll never believe the dreams I had over these last two hours even if I told you."

"Wanna bet? Customers came back here into the

storage room to use the bathroom, stepped over you and your snoring, and came back up front telling me you were talking to butterflies, flying winged creatures, hummingbirds, and that you were mentioning something about an ancient train.

"They also said you spoke of an Amusement Park at Avalon Lake and something about The Five FLAGS of Transformation. I believe it, all right! Now grab your backpack and get into Manhattan before you miss that seminar. What's the name of it anyway?"

That was a great question. With all of these stacks of papers on my desk and other piles of papers and flyers on chairs and in the four corners of the office on the floor, I hadn't recalled the name of the event or seen the flyer in several weeks. I just remembered the start time and the Javits Center location.

I went over to a stack where I kept old personal-growth teaching packets and seminar promotional flyers and saw what I thought to be the flyer for tonight's event. I tugged on the white bottom right corner of the portion of the document sticking out from under several other papers on top and pried it loose from the heap. I was speechless and simply handed the flyer to

Audrey who read the name of the event out loud.

"The Five FLAGS of Transformation."

She handed the paper back to me and said, "All right! Not another word, just get your ass out of here, into your car, and to that event. There's something sacred happening here. Tell me all about it tomorrow. I'll lock up."

I took the flyer, stuffed it into my backpack, and headed out the back door of my store. "Thanks, A," I called out before the door slammed shut.

The drive into Manhattan was quick from here. I'd typically take the train into Grand Central Station but there was no time. It was the Queens Midtown Tunnel that might delay me but if there was anything my dreams of today taught me, it was that I have to accept this present moment as it is and to be okay not knowing. I sat and settled into both of those lessons as the bright moon peeked at me between the skyscrapers of New York City's breathtaking skyline and pulled me gently into its womb.

To be continued ...

Made in the USA
Las Vegas, NV
16 December 2021